Selected Problems on EXCEPTIONAL SETS

by

LENNART CARLESON
University of Uppsala

D. VAN NOSTRAND COMPANY, INC.
PRINCETON, NEW JERSEY
TORONTO LONDON MELBOURNE

Van Nostrand Regional Offices: *New York, Chicago, San Francisco*

D. Van Nostrand Company, Ltd., *London*

D. Van Nostrand Company, (Canada), Ltd., *Toronto*

D. Van Nostrand Australia Pty. Ltd., *Melbourne*

Published simultaneously in Canada by
D. Van Nostrand Company (Canada), Ltd.

PRINTED IN THE UNITED STATES OF AMERICA

PREFACE

In 1959, I prepared a survey of the theory of exceptional sets in a general sense. It was planned to deal with characterizations of "thin" sets by means of capacities, Hausdorff measures, arithmetical conditions etc. and the significance of these concepts to existence problems for harmonic and analytic functions, boundary behaviour, convergence of expansions and to harmonic analysis. -As a preparation, Dr. Hans Wallin checked the literature in Mathematical Reviews 1940–1959 and has here continued up to 1965. The result of his work is contained in the bibliography that should be of value for future research along these lines.

In the meantime, several books have appeared which cover different aspects of the above program. Here should be mentioned:

(1) A. ZYGMUND, Trigonometrical series. 2nd ed. Cambridge 1959;
(2) M. TSUJI, Potential theory in modern function theory. Tokyo 1959;
(3) L. AHLFORS and L. SARIO, Riemann surfaces. Princeton 1960;
(4) G. ALEXITS, Konvergenzprobleme der Orthogonalreihen. Budapest 1960;
(5) J.-P. KAHANE et R. SALEM, Ensembles parfaits et séries trigonométriques. Paris 1963.

In this situation, a survey seemed less desirable. In 1961, I collected, in mimeographed form, those parts that seemed to contain new or less well-known aspects, methods of proof or results. Some further results have been added here. In this way, the result is no survey but the selected problems only reflect the personal interests of the author. Most results are given for d-dimensional Euclidean space and, quite generally, simplicity has been preferred to generality whenever a conflict has arisen.

The references are collected on p. 99 and have no pretension to give a complete description of the background to each problem.

Lennart Carleson

TABLE OF CONTENTS

§ I. *GENERAL CAPACITIES*

1. *Analytic sets.* Suppose that to every finite set of non-negative integers $(n_1, n_2, \ldots, n_p)$ there is associated a *closed* subset $A_{n_1, n_2, \ldots, n_p}$ of a certain fixed bounded set of d-dimensional Euclidean space. All sets considered are thus uniformly bounded. By means of the "Souslin operation" these sets generate a set a,

$$(1.1)\quad a = \bigcup_{n_1, \ldots, n_p, \ldots} A_{n_1} \cap A_{n_1, n_2} \cap \ldots \cap A_{n_1, \ldots, n_p} \cap \ldots .$$

The sets, which arise under this operation for different choices of $\{A_{n_1, \ldots, n_p, \ldots}\}$, are called *analytic*. We observe that we may assume, whenever this is convenient, that

$$A_{n_1, \ldots, n_p, n_{p+1}} \subset A_{n_1, \ldots, n_p} .$$

The following lemma is easily proved.

LEMMA 1. *The family F of analytic sets has the following properties:*

(a) *every closed set belongs to F;*

(b) *if $a^{(k)}$ are analytic, so are $\cap\, a^{(k)}$ and $\cup\, a^{(k)}$.*

Every Borel set is thus analytic.

Proof. (a) is trivial.

(b) If $A^{(k)}_{n_1, \ldots, n_p}$ generate $a^{(k)}$, the union $\cup\, a^{(k)}$ is obtained under the Souslin operation on the sets $A^{(n_1)}_{n_2, \ldots, n_p}$.

To obtain the intersection we put the pairs (k, p) in a sequence by means of the diagonal process. In accordance with this convention we get for a given sequence $n_1, n_2, \ldots$ the following sequence of sets:

$$A_{n_1}^{(1)}, A_{n_1,n_2}^{(1)}, A_{n_3}^{(2)}, A_{n_4}^{(3)}, A_{n_3,n_5}^{(2)}, A_{n_1,n_2,n_6}^{(1)}, \ldots .$$

These sets are called $B_{n_1}, B_{n_1,n_2}, \ldots$. Under the Souslin operation, these sets generate the intersection $\bigcap a^{(k)}$.

Closed subsets of analytic sets are obtained by means of the following lemma.

LEMMA 2. *We assume that* a *is defined above by means of formula* (1.1). $\{h_i\}$ *is an arbitrary sequence of positive integers. We define*

$$F_p = \bigcup_{\substack{n_i \le h_i \\ i \le p}} A_{n_1} \cap A_{n_1,n_2} \cap \ldots \cap A_{n_1,\ldots,n_p}. \tag{1.2}$$

Then

$$F = \bigcap_p F_p \tag{1.3}$$

is a closed subset of a.

Proof. The definitions show that F_p and hence also F are closed sets. To prove $F \subset a$, choose $x \in F$. To every p, there correspond integers n_{ip}, $n_{ip} \le h_i$, and such that

$$x \in A_{n_{1p}} \cap A_{n_{1p},n_{2p}} \cap \ldots \cap A_{n_{1p},\ldots,n_{pp}}.$$

We choose p_ν so that

$$\lim_{\nu\to\infty} n_{ip_\nu} = m_i$$

exist for all i. This is possible since $n_{ip} \le h_i$ and clearly

$$x \in A_{m_1} \cap A_{m_1, m_2} \cap \ldots \cap A_{m_1, \ldots, m_p} \cap \ldots .$$

This implies $x \in a$ and so $F \subset a$.

2. Let $f(E)$ be a non-negative set function, first defined only for compact sets F and then by means of the relation

$$f(E) = \sup_{F \subset E} f(F), \quad F \text{ compact}, \tag{2.1}$$

for all bounded sets E. We also assume

$$f(E_1) \leq f(E_2), \quad \text{if } E_1 \subset E_2. \tag{2.2}$$

Clearly (2.2) need only be assumed for compact sets E. $f(E)$ has the character of an interior measure. We also define an outer measure $f^*(E)$ in the usual way

$$f^*(E) = \inf_{O \supset E} f(O), \quad O \text{ open}. \tag{2.3}$$

This outer measure is assumed to have the following property

$$f^*(E) = \lim_{n\to\infty} f^*(E_n), \quad \text{if } E_n \nearrow E. \tag{2.4}$$

A set function f with the properties (2.1), (2.2) and (2.4) is called a "capacity" and a set E with the property

$$f(E) = f^*(E) \tag{2.5}$$

is called *capacitable*.

THEOREM. *If the compact sets are capacitable, so are all analytic sets.*

Proof. Let E be an analytic set obtained from the family

$A_{n_1,\ldots,n_p}$. Define the set $S^{(h)}$

$$S^{(h)} = \bigcup_{\substack{n_1, n_2, \ldots \\ n_1 \leq h}} A_{n_1} \cap A_{n_1,n_2} \cap \ldots A_{n_1,\ldots,n_j} \cap \ldots .$$

Clearly $S^{(h)} \nearrow E$, $h \nearrow \infty$, and by (2.4) we can for any given $\varepsilon > 0$ choose $h = h_1$ so that $S_1 = S^{(h_1)}$ satisfies

$$f^*(S_1) \geq f^*(E) - \frac{\varepsilon}{2}.$$

Let $S_1, \ldots, S_{p-1}$ be defined and consider

$$S_p^{(h)} = \bigcup_{\substack{n_i \leq h_i,\, i \leq p-1 \\ n_p \leq h}} A_{n_1} \cap A_{n_1,n_2} \cap \ldots \cap A_{n_1,\ldots,n_j} \cap \ldots .$$

Then $f^*(S_p^{(h)}) \nearrow f^*(S_{p-1})$ and $h = h_p$ exists so that

$$S_p = S_p^{(h_p)} \text{ satisfies } f^*(S_p) \geq f^*(S_{p-1}) - \varepsilon \cdot 2^{-p}.$$

It follows that

$$f^*(S_p) \geq f^*(E) - \varepsilon, \quad p = 1, 2, \ldots . \tag{2.6}$$

The sequence h_i being defined we form F_p by means of formula (1.2). The definitions show that $S_p \subset F_p$ and (2.6) and (2.2) imply

$$f^*(F_p) \geq f^*(E) - \varepsilon.$$

F, defined by (1.3), is by Lemma 2 a closed subset of E. On the other hand, let O be an arbitrary open set containing F. Then $O \supset F_p$, if $p \geq p_0$, whence $f(O) \geq f^*(F_{p_0}) \geq f^*(E) - \varepsilon$. Since the closed sets are assumed to be capacitable we find

$$f(E) \geq f(F) = f^*(F) \geq f^*(E) - \varepsilon.$$

The theorem is thus proved.

It should be observed that (2.1), (2.2) and (2.4) do not imply that the closed sets are capacitable as the simple example

$$f(E) = \begin{cases} 1, & \text{if } E \text{ has interior points,} \\ 0 & \text{otherwise} \end{cases}$$

shows.

§ II. *HAUSDORFF MEASURES*

1. Let $h(r)$ be a continuous function defined for $r \geq 0$ with the properties

(1.1) $$h(0) = 0 , \quad h(r) \text{ increasing.}$$

Such a function is called a *measure function*.

Let E be a bounded set. We study all coverings of E with a countable number of spheres S_ν with radii r_ν, that is such that

$$\bigcup_\nu S_\nu \supset E$$

and define

$$M_h(E) = \inf \Sigma\, h(r_\nu)$$

for all such coverings. It is of no importance if S_ν are assumed open or closed. If we also assume $r_\nu \leq \rho$ we get a corresponding lower bound $\Lambda^{(\rho)}$. The limit

$$\Lambda_h(E) = \lim_{\rho \to 0} \Lambda^{(\rho)}$$

clearly exists and is the classical Hausdorff measure of E, possibly and even in general infinite. $M_h(E)$ and $\Lambda_h(E)$ are zero simultaneously. $M_h(E)$ is however more convenient for applications to function theoretic problems.

We shall now introduce an auxiliary function $m_h(E)$. Let G_p denote a net, consisting of intervals with sides 2^{-p}. G_{p+1} is obtained from G_p by subdividing the intervals of G_p into 2^d equal intervals. G is the collection of intervals belonging to any G_p. We cover the set E by intervals $\omega_\nu \in G$, the intervals considered to be closed, and define

$$m_h(E) = \inf \Sigma\, h(\delta_\nu)\,, \tag{1.2}$$

where δ_ν is the side of ω_ν. It is obvious that there exist two positive constants C_1 and C_2, only depending on the dimension of the space, such that

$$C_1\, M_h(E) \leq m_h(E) \leq C_2\, M_h(E). \tag{1.3}$$

2. The importance of the quantity $M_h(E)$ depends on the following theorem.

THEOREM 1. *If* $\mu(e)$ *is a non-negative set function such that*

$$\mu(S) \leq h(r) \tag{2.1}$$

for every sphere S *of radius* r, *then*

$$\mu(E) \leq M_h(E)\,. \tag{2.2}$$

Conversely, there is a constant a, *only depending on the dimension, such that for every compact set* F, *there is a* μ *with the property (2.1) such that*

$$\mu(F) \geq a\, M_h(F)\,. \tag{2.3}$$

Proof. That (2.1) implies (2.2) follows immediately from the definitions. Let $\{S_\nu\}$ satisfy $\cup\, S_\nu \supset E$. Then

$$\mu(E) \leq \mu(\cup\, S_\nu) \leq \Sigma\, \mu(S_\nu) \leq \Sigma\, h(r_\nu)\,.$$

For the construction of μ with the property (2.3), we fix an integer n and construct $\mu_n(e)$ such that $\mu(\omega_n) = h(2^{-n})$ for all $\omega_n \in G_n$ for which $\omega_n \cap F \neq \phi$. We let μ have constant density on each $\omega_n \in G_n$. If for some $\omega_{n-1} \in G_{n-1}$,

$$\mu_n(\omega_{n-1}) > h(2^{-n+1}),$$

we reduce the density of μ on the corresponding ω_n's so that the mass on ω_{n-1} becomes $h(2^{-n+1})$. The resulting set function is called μ_{n-1}. We treat μ_{n-1} in a similar way and after n steps we have obtained the set function μ_0. This function has the property

$$\mu_0(\omega_\nu) \leq h(2^{-\nu}), \quad \omega_\nu \in G_\nu, \quad \nu \leq n.$$

The original choice of n determines μ_0, which is now denoted $\mu_0^{(n)}$. Let $n \to \infty$ and choose a weakly convergent subsequence: $\mu_0^{(n_i)} \to \mu$, $i \to \infty$. μ has its support on F and satisfies

$$\mu(\omega_\nu) \leq 2^d h(2^{-\nu}), \quad \omega_\nu \in G_\nu. \tag{2.4}$$

On the other hand, let $\bigcup_{j=1}^{N} \omega^{(j)} \supset F$, $\omega^{(j)} \in G$ and $\omega^{(j)} \cap F \neq \phi$. Let n be large enough and consider $\mu_0 = \mu_0^{(n)}$. The reduction from μ_n to μ_0 is such that either $\mu_0(\omega^{(j)}) = h(\delta^{(j)})$ or $\Sigma^* \mu_0(\omega^{(j)}) = h(\delta)$, where the summation Σ^* is taken over all $\omega^{(j)} \subset$ a certain $\omega \in G$ of side δ. Hence the total mass of μ_0 is $\geq \inf \Sigma h(\delta_\nu)$, for all *finite* sums. The same inequality then also holds for μ. If we drop the restriction to finite sums we get the smaller lower bound $m_h(F)$. Hence

$$\mu_0(F) \geq m_h(F),$$

which together with (2.4) proves the theorem.

3. $M_h(E)$ is easily seen to be an outer measure:

$$M_h(E) = \inf_{O \supset E} M_h(O), \quad O \text{ open}.$$

This need not hold for the set function $m_h(E)$. It is however clearly true for $d = 1$ and in order to make the argument clear we first consider *linear* sets.

If then $d = 1$ and $h(r)$ is an arbitrary measure function, we thus have

$$(3.1) \qquad m_h(E) = \inf_{O \supset E} m_h(O).$$

We shall now prove

$$(3.2) \qquad \lim_{n\to\infty} m_h(E_n) = m_h(E), \quad E_n \nearrow E.$$

Let $\{\varepsilon_n\}$ be a sequence of positive numbers to be specified later and choose a covering $\{\omega_{\nu n}\}$ of E_n such that

$$(3.3) \qquad \sum_{\nu} h(\delta_{\nu n}) < m_h(E_n) + \varepsilon_n.$$

For every $x \in E$, let ω be the largest interval $\omega_{\nu n}$ containing x. We also assume, as we may, that $k/2^n \notin E$, for all integers k and n. The different non-intersecting intervals ω —countably many—that we obtain in this way, are denoted ω_μ of lengths δ_μ. Obviously

$$E \subset \cup \omega_\mu.$$

We now choose an integer m and consider first those ω_μ's that are taken from $\{\omega_{\nu 1}\}$. They cover a certain subset Q_1 of E_m. The same subset is covered by a certain subsequence of $\{\omega_{\nu m}\}$, denoted $\{\omega_{\nu m}\}^{(1)}$. These intervals are subintervals of the chosen ω_μ's. These intervals ω_μ also cover the smaller set $Q_1 \cap E_1$ and the sum $\Sigma^{(1)} h(\delta_\mu)$ can, by (3.3) for $n = 1$, be diminished by at most ε_1. Hence we find

$$\Sigma^{(1)}h(\delta_\mu) \leq \Sigma^{(1)}h(\delta_{\nu m}) + \varepsilon_1 . \tag{3.4}$$

We then consider ω_μ's taken from $\{\omega_{\nu 2}\}$ but not from $\{\omega_{\nu 1}\}$. As above we find

$$\Sigma^{(2)}h(\delta_\mu) \leq \Sigma^{(2)}h(\delta_{\nu m}) + \varepsilon_2 . \tag{3.5}$$

We repeat the argument until all coverings $\{\omega_{\nu n}\}$, $n \leq m$, have been considered. The m inequalities (3.4), (3.5), . . . , are added which yields

$$\sum_{n=1}^{m} \Sigma^{(n)}h(\delta_\mu) \leq \Sigma\, h(\delta_{\nu m}) + \sum_1^m \varepsilon_\nu \leq m_h(E_m) + \sum_1^m \varepsilon_\nu + \varepsilon_m .$$

We let $m \to \infty$ and find

$$\Sigma\, h(\delta_\mu) \leq \lim_{m\to\infty} m_h(E_m) + \sum_1^\infty \varepsilon_\nu .$$

Since $\sum_1^\infty \varepsilon_\nu$ can be chosen arbitrarily small we find

$$m_h(E) \leq \lim_{m\to\infty} m_h(E_n) .$$

Since the opposite inequality is trivial we have proved (3.2).

If we specialize E_n to be compact and E to be open and bounded (3.2) implies

$$m_h(O) = \sup_{F\subset O} m_h(F) . \tag{3.6}$$

If we choose $f(F) = m_h(F)$ for compact sets F, (3.6) and (3.1) show that $m_h(E) = f^*(E)$ for all sets. (3.2) is then condition (2.4) of section I. (3.1) means that the compact sets are capacitable and hence by the theorem of § I all analytic sets are capacitable. The most interesting consequence of this fact is formulated in the following theorem.

THEOREM 2. *An analytic set of positive Hausdorff measure for some measure function* h *contains a closed subset also of positive* h*-measure.*

So far, we have only proved the result for linear sets. If a $(d-1)$-dimensional hyperplane has h-measure zero, the above argument applies without any change. To obtain the general result, we give the word "covering" a slightly changed meaning: the system $\{\omega\}$ "covers" E if every point of E is an interior point of $\cup\,\omega$. The corresponding lower bound (1.2) is denoted $m_h'(E)$. It is obvious that the inequality (1.3) holds also for m_h' and that m_h' is an outer measure in the sense of (3.1). An inspection of the proof of (3.2) shows that this relation also is true. These two relations give Theorem 2. We do not carry out the detailed proof.

4. An interesting consequence of Theorem 2 is

THEOREM 3. *Every analytic set* E *of positive Hausdorff measure contains a closed subset such that*

$$0 < \Lambda_h(F) < \infty\,, \quad F \subset E\,.$$

Proof. As before, the proof is simpler in the linear case. We therefore assume, for the moment, that $d = 1$.

Suppose that $E \supset F_1 \supset F_2 \supset \ldots \supset F_n$, with F_ν closed, have been constructed such that

$$m_h(F_\nu) = a_\nu\,, \quad \nu = 1, 2, \ldots, n\,, \tag{4.1}$$

and

(4.2) $$\inf \Sigma h(\delta^{(j)}) = b_\nu, \quad \delta^{(j)} \leq 2^{-\nu}, \quad \cup \omega^{(j)} \supset F_\nu.$$

By Theorem 2, F_1 with $a_1 > 0$ exists.

Let $m = m(n)$ be a sufficiently large integer to be specified later. Choose a covering of F_n satisfying the conditions of (4.2) and such that

$$\sum_j h(\delta^{(j)}) \leq b_n + 2^{-n}.$$

As remarked before, we may assume that the covering is finite $j \leq N$. If $\delta^{(1)} < 2^{-n}$, or if $\delta^{(1)} = 2^{-n}$ and $m_h(\delta^{(1)} \cap F_n) < h(2^{-n})$, we do not change F_n inside $\delta^{(1)}$. Otherwise we remove from $\delta^{(1)}$ its subintervals $\omega_m \in G_m$, here considered as open (or half-open for its end-intervals), one at a time and consider the intersection of the remaining closed set with F_n. We must reach a first point when the m_h-measure of this intersection A_1 is smaller than $h(2^{-n})$. Then

(4.3) $$h(2^{-n}) - h(2^{-m}) \leq m_h(A_1) < h(2^{-n}).$$

We treat in a similar way $\delta^{(2)}, \ldots, \delta^{(N)}$ and obtain the sets $A_2, \ldots, A_N$. We now choose

$$F_{n+1} = \bigcup_{\nu=1}^{N} A_\nu.$$

From the definition (4.2) it follows that

(4.4) $$b_{n+1} \leq b_n + 2^{-n}.$$

On the other hand, when we consider coverings of F_{n+1} by arbitrary intervals $\omega^{(j)}$, F_{n+1} does not differ from F_n as far as intervals $\omega^{(j)}$ of length $\geq 2^{-n}$ are concerned. For subintervals of $\delta^{(j)}$ we have the inequalities (4.3). Hence

$$a_{n+1} \geq a_n - N \cdot h(2^{-m}). \tag{4.5}$$

Choosing m large enough we get $\lim_{n\to\infty} a_n > 0$ while $\overline{\lim}\, b_n < \infty$. We now define

$$F = \bigcap_{n=1}^{\infty} F_n.$$

Then $\Lambda_h(F) \leq \lim b_n < \infty$ while $m_h(F) > 0$ since we need only consider finite coverings.

The proof goes through without change if E does not intersect the hyperplanes used in the construction of the nets G_n. If an intersection has h-measure zero we may remove it without changing $m_h(E)$. Therefore the only alternative is that $m_h(E \cap H) > 0$ for some hyperplane H. We have then reduced the dimension of the problem and can repeat the considerations. The result is therefore generally valid.

§ III. *POTENTIAL THEORY*

1. Let $H(t)$ be a non-negative, continuous, increasing, convex function of the real variable t, $-\infty < t < \infty$. Let $\phi(r)$, $r = |x|$, be a fundamental solution of Laplace's equation

$$\phi(r) = \begin{cases} \log \frac{1}{r}, & d = 2 \\ r^{2-d}, & d \neq 2. \end{cases}$$

We shall, in order to keep a good balance between generality and simplicity, only study kernels $K(r)$ of the form

$$K(r) = H(\phi(r)).$$

We also assume

$$\int_0 K(r)\, r^{d-1}\, dr < \infty.$$

With respect to $K(r)$ we form the potential of the real completely additive set function σ,

$$u_\sigma(x) = \int K(|x-y|)\, d\sigma(y)$$

and the energy integral

$$I(\sigma) = \int\int K(|x-y|) d\sigma(x)\, d\sigma(y).$$

For σ with a variable sign we study $I(\sigma)$ only when $I(|\sigma|) < \infty$.

If we restrict ourselves to non-negative measures μ with bounded support, u and I have the following properties of semi-continuity.

LEMMA 1.

(a) $\varliminf_{x \to x_0} u_\mu(x) \geq u_\mu(x_0)$.

If $\mu_n \to \mu$ *weakly then*

(b) $\varliminf_{n \to \infty} u_{\mu_n}(x) \geq u_\mu(x)$;

(c) $\varliminf I(\mu_n) \geq I(\mu)$.

Proof. The relations follow immediately from the definitions.

THEOREM 1 (The maximum principle). *If* $u_\mu(x) \leq 1$ *on the support* S_μ *of* μ, *then* $u_\mu(x) \leq 1$ *everywhere.*

Proof. By Egoroff's theorem there is a closed subset F of S_μ such that, for a given $\varepsilon > 0$,

$$\mu(F) > \mu(S_\mu) - \varepsilon \tag{1.1}$$

and such that $u_\mu(x)$ converges uniformly on F. If we define $\mu_1(e) = \mu(e \cap F)$, then clearly $u_{\mu_1}(x)$ converges uniformly on F, i.e., for any $x_0 \in F$

$$\int\limits_{|y - x_0| < \eta} K(|y - x_0|)\, d\mu_1(y) < \delta , \quad \eta = \eta(\delta).$$

Let $\{x_n\}$ be a sequence such that $x_n \to x_0 \in F$. Then

$$\varlimsup_{n \to \infty} u_{\mu_1}(x_n) \leq \int\limits_{|y - x_0| \geq \eta} K(|y - x_0|)\, d\mu_1(y) + \tag{1.2}$$

$$+ \varlimsup_{n \to \infty} \int\limits_{|y - x_n| < \eta} K(|y - x_n|)\, d\mu_1(y).$$

Now there is a number N, only depending on d, with the following property. For any x there are N overlapping closed cones Q_ν with vertices at x such that if ξ_ν is the point of $Q_\nu \cap F$ which is closest to x, then any other point $y \in F$ is closer to some ξ_ν than to x. If ξ_ν are chosen for $x = x_n$, this means that

$$K(|y - x_n|) \leq \sum_{\nu=1}^{N} K(|y - \xi_\nu|, \quad y \in F, \quad \xi_\nu \in F.$$

The last term of (1.2) is thus $\leq N\delta$, and we have proved

$$\overline{\lim_{x\to x_0}}\; u_{\mu_1}(x) \leq u_{\mu_1}(x_0).$$

By Lemma 1(a), $u_{\mu_1}(x)$ is continuous in the entire space and since it is subharmonic outside F, we have $u_{\mu_1}(x) \leq 1$.

Finally, let z be an arbitrary point, $z \notin S_\mu$. Then if ρ is the distance from z to S_μ, we have

$$u_\mu(z) \leq u_{\mu_1}(z) + \varepsilon K(\rho) \leq 1 + \varepsilon K(\rho).$$

We now let $\varepsilon \to 0$ and obtain the desired result.

The proof of Theorem 1 contains the following result.

THEOREM 2 (The continuity principle). *If $u_\mu(x)$ is continuous on S_μ, then $u_\mu(x)$ is continuous everywhere.*

Proof. We need only observe that by Dini's theorem, the integrals are uniformly convergent on S_μ.

2. *Capacity.* Let E be a bounded Borel set and Γ_E the class of distributions of mass on E, i.e., non-negative set functions μ with $S_\mu \subset E$, with the property

$$u_\mu(x) \leq 1, \quad x \in E. \tag{2.1}$$

Equivalently we may assume (2.1) for all x. The capacity $C_K(E)$ of E is defined by the relation

$$\sup_{\mu\in\Gamma_E} \mu(E) = C_K(E). \tag{2.2}$$

A property that holds except on a set of capacity zero, is said to hold p.p. Observe that if u_ν is a bounded potential, then ν vanishes for sets of capacity zero.

The notion of equilibrium is closely related to the concept of capacity. We shall first show the existence of equilibrium distributions in the following form.

THEOREM 3. *Let F be a compact set and assume that for every point $x \in F$ there is a bounded half-cone $V_x \subset F$. If furthermore*

$$\frac{K(r)}{K(2r)} = O(1), \quad r \to 0, \tag{2.3}$$

$\mu \in \Gamma_F$ exists so that $u_\mu(x) \equiv 1$ on F and $\mu(F) = C_K(F)$.

Proof. We study the variational problem

$$\gamma = \inf I(\mu), \quad S_\mu \subset F, \quad \mu(F) = 1.$$

By Lemma 1(c), the lower bound γ is assumed for a certain distribution of unit mass μ. We shall prove that $u_\mu \equiv \gamma$ on F.

1) *$u_\mu(x) \geq \gamma$ on F except on a set of capacity zero.*

Let us namely assume that $u_\mu(x) < \gamma - \varepsilon$ on $T \subset F$, $C(T) > 0$. Let τ be a distribution of unit mass on T so that $u_\tau(x) \leq K$ and form

$$\mu_\delta = (1-\delta)\mu + \delta\tau$$

so that $\mu_\delta \in \Gamma_F$ and $\mu_\delta(F) = 1$. We find

$$I(\mu\delta) \leq I(\mu) - 2\delta\, I(\mu) + 2\delta \int u_\mu \, d\tau + O(\delta^2) \leq$$
$$\leq \gamma - 2\delta\gamma + 2\delta(\gamma - \varepsilon) + O(\delta^2) \leq$$
$$\leq \gamma - 2\delta\varepsilon + O(\delta^2) < \gamma$$

if $\delta > 0$ is small enough.

2) $u_\mu(x) \leq \gamma$ *on* S_μ *and so everywhere.*

Since a set e with $\mu(e) > 0$ has positive capacity, 1) implies that $u_\mu(x) \geq \gamma$ on S_μ except on a set where μ vanishes. If $u_\mu(x_0) > \gamma$, $x_0 \in S_\mu$, then $u_\mu(x) > \gamma$ in a neighbourhood of x_0 which must have positive μ-measure. This contradicts, however, $I(\mu) = \gamma$.

3) *If (2.3) holds and* V_x *exists, then* $u_\mu(x) = \gamma$.

Let $x = 0$ be such a point in F and let Q be the cone V_x. Let a and b, $a < b$, be real numbers, sufficiently small, and define

$$q(x) = \begin{cases} \dfrac{K(|x|)}{\int_{|y|<|x|} K(|y|)dy}, & x \in Q, \quad a < |x| < b \\ 0 & \text{otherwise}. \end{cases}$$

There exist arbitrarily small numbers a and b so that

$$\int_{-\infty}^{\infty} q(x)dx = 1.$$

By 1) and 2) we find

$$\gamma = \int u_\mu(x)\, q(x)dx = \int_F d\mu(y) \int K(|x-y|)\, q(x)dx. \tag{2.4}$$

Let $\rho > 0$ be a fixed number. When $a, b \to 0$ we have uniformly

$$\int K(|x-y|)\, q(x)dx \to K(|y|), \quad |y| > \rho.$$

Furthermore we have, $|y| \leq \rho$,

$$\int_{a<|x|<b} \frac{K(|x|)\, K(|x-y|)}{\int_{|t|<|x|} K(|t|)dt}\, dx \leq \text{Const. } K(|\tfrac{y}{2}|) \leq \text{Const. } K(|y|)$$

by (2.3).

This implies

$$\int_{|y|<\rho} d\mu(y) \int K(|x-y|)q(x)dx \leq \text{Const.} \int_{|y|<\rho} K(|y|)d\mu(y) < \delta(\rho),$$

where $\delta(\rho) \to 0$, $\rho \to 0$, since by 2) $\int K(|y|)d\mu(y) < \infty$. If first $a, b \to 0$, and then $\rho \to 0$ we find $u_\mu(0) = \gamma$.

Let us now choose $\mu_0 = \gamma^{-1}\mu$. Then $u_{\mu_0} \equiv 1$ on F and $\mu_0 \in \Gamma_F$. Finally suppose $\nu \in \Gamma_F$. Then

$$\mu_0(F) \geq \int u_\nu(x)\, d\mu_0(x) = \int u_{\mu_0}(x)\, d\nu(x) = \nu(F).$$

This inequality completes the proof of Theorem 3.

For an arbitrary kernel $K(|x|)$ and an arbitrary compact set we have the following theorem.

THEOREM 4. *For any kernel $K(|x|)$ and any compact set F, there exists $\mu \in \Gamma_F$ so that*

$$u_\mu(x) = 1 \quad p.p. \text{ on } \quad F$$

and

$$\mu(F) = C_K(F).$$

This follows immediately from 1) and 2) in the proof of Theorem 3.

THEOREM 5. *The extremal problems*

$$\begin{array}{llll} A^{-1} & = \inf\limits_{\nu} I(\nu)\,, & & S_\nu \subset F\,,\ \ \nu(F) = 1\,, \\ B & = \inf\limits_{\nu}\ \{\text{total mass of } \nu\}\,, & & u_\nu \geq 1 \ \ \textit{p.p. on } F \\ C & = \sup \nu(F)\,, & & u_\nu \leq 1 \ \ \textit{p.p. on } F \end{array}$$

are equivalent so that

$$A = B = C = C_K(F)\,.$$

Proof. Let μ be the distribution of Theorem 4.

(A) By 1) and 2) in the proof of Theorem 3, a solution ν of the A-problem has the property $u_\nu = A^{-1}$ p.p. on F and $u_\nu \leq A^{-1}$ everywhere. Hence

$$\frac{C_K(F)}{A} = \int u_\nu \, d\mu = \int u_\mu \, d\nu = 1$$

since a distribution with a bounded potential vanishes for all sets of capacity zero.

(B) If $u_\nu \geq 1$ p.p. on F, then

$$C_K(F) \leq \int u_\nu \, d\mu = \int u_\mu \, d\nu \leq \int d\nu\,.$$

Hence

$$B \geq C_K(F)\,.$$

The opposite inequality is obvious.

(C) If $u_\nu \leq 1$ p.p. on F, then

$$C_K(F) \geq \int_F u_\nu \, d\mu = \int_F u_\mu \, d\nu \geq \nu(F)\,.$$

Again, the opposite inequality is obvious.

THEOREM 6. *The solution of the extremal problems* (A) *and* (C) *of Theorem 5 is unique and identical for the two problems.*

We observe that problem (B) need not have a unique solution as this example for $d = 2$ shows:

$$F\colon x^2 + y^2 = 1\,, \qquad K(r) = \overset{+}{\log}\,\frac{2}{r}\,,$$

μ_1: uniform on F; μ_2: mass concentration at $(0,0)$.

The proof of Theorem 6 is by means of Fourier transformations. It should be observed that it is here an advantage to deal with general kernels, since we may assume $K(r) \equiv 0$, $r > r_0$. The case $K = \log \frac{1}{r}$. $d = 2$, requires a special simple treatment which we omit here. We first prove two lemmas.

LEMMA 2. *Suppose* $K(r) \equiv 0$, $r > r_0$. *Then, for* $d \geq 2$,

$$F(\xi) = \int_{-\infty}^{\infty} K(r) e^{i(x,\xi)} dx > 0\,, \quad \textit{all} \quad \xi,\ r = |x|\,.$$

For $d = 1$, $F(\xi) = 0$ *can hold at isolated points.*

Proof. Let Σ denote the unit sphere and $d\sigma$ its area-element, normalized so that $\sigma(\Sigma) = 1$. $F(\xi)$ is clearly a function of $|\xi|$ only and to simplify the notations we assume $|\xi| = 1$. We have, c_ν denoting positive constants only depending on d,

$$F(\xi) = c_1 \int_0^{\infty} K(r) r^{n-1} dr \int_{\Sigma} e^{irx_1} d\sigma_x = c_1 \int_0^{\infty} K(r) J(r) r^{n-1} dr\,, |\xi| = 1\,.$$

The function $J(t)$ can be written

$$J(t) = \begin{cases} c_2 \operatorname{Re} \left\{ \int_0^{\pi/2} e^{it\cos\phi} \sin^{d-2}\phi \, d\phi \right\}, & d \geq 2 \\ \cos t\,, & d = 1\,. \end{cases}$$

It is easy to prove (and of course well known) that $J(t)$ has the following properties:

$$\begin{cases} J(0) = 1, \quad J'(0) = 0; \\ J(t) < 1; \quad t \neq 0, \quad d \geq 2; \quad t \neq 2\pi n, \quad d = 1; \\ J(t) = -J''(t) - \frac{d-1}{t} J'(t). \end{cases}$$

If the last expression is inserted in the formula for $F(\xi)$, $|\xi| = 1$, we get, using the first property of J in the partial integrations,

$$F(\xi) = -c_1 \int_0^\infty K(r)\,[(d-1)r^{d-2}J' + r^{d-1}J'']\,dr =$$

$$= c_1 \int_0^\infty K' r^{d-1} J' dr = c_1 \int_0^\infty (1-J)\, d(K' r^{d-1}).$$

The convexity assumption on K is equivalent to $d(K'r^{d-1}) \geq 0$. By the second property of J and the fact that $d(K'r^{d-1}) \equiv 0$ is excluded we get the assertion for $d \geq 2$. The case $d = 1$ is easily proved.

LEMMA 3. *For all kernels K considered and all $\sigma \not\equiv 0$ with compact support such that $I(|\sigma|) < \infty$, $I(\sigma) > 0$ holds.*

Proof. Since σ has compact support we may assume that $K(r) \equiv 0$, $r > r_0$. We write

$$I(\sigma) = \int u(x)\, d\sigma(x), \quad u(x) = \int K(|x-y|)\, d\sigma(y).$$

Denoting the (suitably normalized) Fourier transforms of u, K and $d\sigma$ $\hat{u}, \hat{K}$, and $\hat{\sigma}$ respectively, we find $\hat{u}(\xi) = \hat{K}(\xi)\,\hat{\sigma}(\xi)$ and—formally—by Parseval's relation

$$I(\sigma) = \int \hat{K}(\xi)\, |\hat{\sigma}(\xi)|^2\, d\xi.$$

To justify this formula, let σ_1 be a restriction of σ so that

$|I(\sigma) - I(\sigma_1)| < \varepsilon$ and u_{σ_1} is continuous. To see that σ_1 exists, set $\sigma - \sigma_1 = \tau$. Then

$$|I(\sigma) - I(\sigma_1)| \leq |2 \int u_{\sigma_1} d\tau| + |I(\tau)| < 3 \int u_{|\sigma|}\, d|\tau|$$

and the last expression tends to zero with $\int d|\tau|$. Let $\phi_n(x)$ be $\gamma_n \exp\{-n|x|^2\}$, normalized so that $\int \phi_n(x)dx = 1$. Then $\hat{\phi}_n > 0$ and clearly by Parseval's formula

$$\int \hat{\phi}_n(\xi)\, \hat{K}(\xi)\, |\hat{\sigma}_1(\xi)|^2 d\xi = \int \phi_n * u_{\sigma_1}(x)\, d\sigma_1(x).$$

Since by Lemma 1 $\hat{\phi}_n \hat{K} \geq 0$ we can first let $n \to \infty$ and then $\varepsilon \to 0$ and obtain the desired formula for $I(\sigma)$.

By Lemma 1 $I(\sigma) \geq 0$. If $I(\sigma) = 0$ we must have $\hat{\sigma}(\xi) \equiv 0$, that is $\sigma \equiv 0$.

Proof of Theorem 6.

(A) Every solution of $\inf I(\mu)$, $\mu(F) = 1$, has by Theorem 2 the properties

$$u_\mu \leq C_K(F)^{-1} \quad \text{everywhere}$$

$$u_\mu = C_K(F)^{-1} \quad \text{p.p. on } F.$$

Let μ_1 and μ_2 be two extremals. Then

$$I(\mu_1 - \mu_2) = I(\mu_1) - 2 \int u_{\mu_1} d\mu_2 + I(\mu_2) = 0,$$

since μ_2 vanishes on the set where $u_{\mu_1} < C_K(F)^{-1}$.

(C) Assume that $u_\nu \leq 1$ and that $\nu(F) = C_K(F)$. Let μ be the unique solution of (A). Then

$$I(\mu - \nu) = \int u_\nu\, d\nu - 2 \int u_\mu\, d\nu + I(\mu) \leq$$

$$\leq C_K(F) - 2\, C_K(F) + C_K(F) = 0.$$

3. The definition shows that $C_K(E)$ satisfies the relations (2.1) and (2.2) of section I. The corresponding outer measure (I.2.3) is denoted $C_K^*(E)$. We shall show that the conditions of Theorem I are fulfilled so that the following theorem holds.

THEOREM 7. *Every analytic set is capacitable for the set function* $C_K(E)$.

Proof. 1) *The compact sets are capacitable for* $C_K(E)$.

Let F be a compact set and let O_n be the set of points x with distance $< n^{-1}$ to F. Let $\mu_n \in \Gamma_{O_n}$ be such that $\mu_n(O_n) > C_K(O_n) - n^{-1}$. Since $\mu_n(O_n)$ clearly are bounded, there is a weakly convergent sequence $\mu_{n_\nu} \to \mu$. By Lemma 1 (b), $\mu \in \Gamma_F$. Since

$$\mu(F) = \lim_{\nu\to\infty} \mu_{n_\nu}(O_{n_\nu}) = \lim_{n\to\infty} C_K(O_n),$$

we have

$$C_K(F) \geq C_K^*(F).$$

2) *If* $E_n \nearrow E$, *then* $C_K^*(E_n) \nearrow C_K^*(E)$.

The proof of this statement requires a number of lemmas. All sets used are assumed to be contained in a fixed bounded set M.

LEMMA 4. *For any sets* E_n

$$C_K\Big(\bigcup_{n=1}^{\infty} E_n\Big) \leq \sum_1^{\infty} C_K(E_n).$$

Proof. Choose $\mu \in \Gamma_{\cup E_n}$. We can write $\mu = \sum_1^{\infty} \mu_n$ where μ_n is the restriction of μ to E_n or, if $\{E_n\}$ have common points, to a subset of E_n. Clearly $\mu_n \in \Gamma_{E_n}$, which yields the lemma.

LEMMA 5. *For any sets* E_n

$$C_K^*(\bigcup_{n=1}^{\infty} E_n) \leq \sum_{n=1}^{\infty} C_K^*(E_n).$$

Proof. Choose $O_n \supset E_n$ so that $C_K(O_n) \leq C_K^*(E_n) + \varepsilon \cdot 2^{-n}$. By Lemma 2

$$C_K(\bigcup_1^{\infty} O_n) \leq \sum_{n=1}^{\infty} C_K^*(E_n) + \varepsilon.$$

The lemma is proved.

LEMMA 6. *If $u_\mu(x) \leq 1$, there exists for any $\varepsilon > 0$ an open set O such that $C_K(O) < \varepsilon$ and such that $u_\mu(x)$ is continuous on the complement O' of O.*

Proof. By the proof of Theorem 1, there exists for any $\delta > 0$ a restriction μ_1 of μ so that $u_{\mu_1}(x)$ is continuous and

$$u_\mu(x) = u_{\mu_1}(x) + u_\nu(x)$$

and

$$\nu(M) < \delta.$$

The set S_n where $u_\nu(x) > n^{-1}$ is by Lemma 1 (a) open and

$$C^*(S_n) = C(S_n) \leq n\,\delta,$$

for if $\lambda \in \Gamma_{S_n}$ we have

$$\delta > \int u_\lambda \, d\nu = \int u_\nu \, d\lambda > n^{-1} \lambda(S_n).$$

Choose n_i and δ_i so that $\sum_i n_i \delta_i < \varepsilon$. The set

$$O = \bigcup_i S_{n_i}$$

is open and by Lemma 2 $C(O) < \varepsilon$. Since for every $\delta > 0$ $u_{\mu_1}(x)$ is continuous, it follows that the oscillation of $u_\mu(x)$ at a point outside S_n is $< n^{-1}$. Hence $u_\mu(x)$ is continuous outside O.

LEMMA 7. *If $\mu_n \to \mu$ weakly, then*

$$\underline{\lim}_{n \to \infty} u_{\mu_n}(x) = u_\mu(x)$$

except in a set of exterior capacity zero.

Proof. Given $\varepsilon > 0$, there is by Lemmas 4 and 6 an open set O so that u_{μ_n}, $n = 1, 2, \ldots,$ and u_μ are continuous outside O and $C_K(O) < \varepsilon$. Let r and ρ be rational numbers, $r < \rho$, and consider the set F_n:

$$F_n = \{x \mid u_{\mu_n}(x) \geq r, \quad u_\mu(x) \leq \rho, \quad x \in O'\}.$$

F_n is closed and so is then

$$\Phi_n = \bigcap_{\nu=n}^{\infty} F_\nu .$$

We shall first show that

$$C_K(\Phi_n) = 0. \tag{3.1}$$

If (3.1) does not hold, there exists $\nu \in \Gamma\Phi_n$ so that $\nu \not\equiv 0$ and $u_\nu(x)$ is continuous for all x. We find

$$0 = \lim_{n \to \infty} \int u_\nu(x)\, d(\mu - \mu_n) = \lim_{n \to \infty} \int (u_\mu(x) - u_{\mu_n}(x))\, d\nu(x) \geq (\rho - r)\, \nu(\Phi_n)$$

This contradiction proves (3.1).

It now follows from (3.1) and Lemma 5 that

$$C_K^*\Big(\bigcup_{r,\rho} \bigcup_n \Phi_n\Big) \leq \sum_{r,\rho,n} C_K^*(\Phi_n) = 0 .$$

The set $\bigcup_{r,\rho,n} \Phi_n$ contains however the exceptional set of Lemma 7 and this lemma is thus proved.

LEMMA 8. *To an open set* O *there corresponds a mass distribution* μ *such that*

(a) $u_\mu = 1$ *on* O *except on a set of exterior capacity zero.*

(b) $u_\mu \leq 1$

(c) $\mu(M) = C_K(O)$.

Proof. Let $F_n \nearrow O$ and suppose that $u_{\mu_n} = 1$ p.p. on F_n and $\mu_n(F_n) \nearrow C_K(O)$, $\mu_n \to \mu$. The subset of F_n where $u_{\mu_n} \leq 1 - k^{-1}$ is a closed set of capacity zero and hence by 1) of exterior capacity zero. Since this holds for every k, it follows from Lemma 5 that $u_{\mu_n} = 1$ except on a set of exterior capacity zero. We now use Lemma 7 and again Lemma 5 and deduce that μ has all properties (a), (b) and (c) of Lemma 8.

We can now complete the proof of Theorem 7. Let $E_n \nearrow E$ and choose $O_n \supset E_n$ and with O_n also μ_n of Lemma 8.

$$\mu_n(M) = C_K(O_n) \leq C_K^*(E_n) + n^{-1}.$$

We assume that $\mu_n \to \mu$ so that, by Lemma 7, $u_\mu = 1$ on E except on a set S of exterior capacity zero and $\mu_n(M) \leq \lim C_K^*(E_n)$. Let O_ε be the open set where $u_\mu > 1 - \varepsilon$, $O_\varepsilon \supset E - S$. Hence

$$C_K^*(E) \leq C_K^*(E - S) + C_K^*(S) \leq C_K(O_\varepsilon) \leq \frac{\mu(M)}{1-\varepsilon} \leq$$

$$\leq \lim_{n\to\infty} C_K^*(E_n) \cdot (1 - \varepsilon)^{-1}.$$

Thus

$$C_K^*(E) \leq \lim_{n\to\infty} C_K^*(E_n).$$

§ IV. *CERTAIN PROPERTIES OF HAUSDORFF MEASURES AND CAPACITIES*

1. There is a close connexion between Hausdorff measures and capacities which is exhibited by the following theorem.

THEOREM 1. *For any bounded set* E, $C_K(E) > 0$ *implies* $\Lambda_{\overline{K}-1}(E) = \infty$, *where*

$$\overline{K}(r) = r^{-d} \int_0^r K(t)\, t^{d-1}\, dt \, .$$

If conversely E *is analytic and* $\Lambda_h(E) > 0$ *for a measure function* h *such that*

$$\int_0 K(r)\, dh(r) < \infty \, , \tag{1.1}$$

then $C_K(E) > 0$.

Proof. 1) Assume $C_K(E) > 0$, so that $\mu \not\equiv 0$ concentrated on $F \subset E$ exists with $u_\mu(x) \le 1$. The restriction μ_1 of μ to a suitable $F_1 \subset F$, $\mu_1 \not\equiv 0$, corresponds to a uniformly continuous potential u_{μ_1}. Then, by Dini's theorem, there exists another kernel $K_1(r)$ such that

$$\lim_{r \to 0} \frac{K(r)}{K_1(r)} = 0 \tag{1.2}$$

and such that

$$\int K_1(|x-y|)\, d\mu_1(y) \le M \tag{1.3}$$

for all x. Now let $\{S_\nu\}$ be a finite covering of F_1 by open spheres $|x - x_\nu| < r_\nu$ and assume $r_\nu \leq \rho$. Then forming mean-values over spheres with twice the radius we find, by (1.3), for a certain constant M_1,

$$\mu_1(F_1) \leq \Sigma\, \mu_1(S_\nu) \leq \Sigma \frac{M_1}{\overline{\overline{K}}_1(r_\nu)} \leq M_1 \sup_{r \leq \rho} \frac{\overline{K}(r)}{\overline{\overline{K}}_1(r)} \sum_\nu \frac{1}{\overline{K}(r_\nu)} .$$

We now use (1.2). The above inequality then implies for a certain $\varepsilon(\rho) \to 0$, $\rho \to 0$,

$$\Lambda^{(\rho)}_{\overline{K}-1} \geq \frac{\mu_1(F)}{M_1 \varepsilon(\rho)} .$$

Letting $\rho \to 0$ we find $\Lambda_{\overline{K}-1}(E) = \infty$ as asserted.

2) Since E is analytic there is a closed set F with $M_h(F) > 0$. Hence, by Theorem II.1, there is a mass distribution μ on F such that II.2.1 holds. Choose an arbitrary point x_0 and set

$$\phi(r) = \mu(\{x \mid |x - x_0| < r\}) .$$

Then, assuming as we may that $K \equiv 0$, $r > r_0$,

$$\begin{aligned} u_\mu(x_0) &= \int K(r)\, d\phi(r) = -\int \phi(r)\, dK(r) \leq \\ &\leq -\int h(r)\, dK(r) = \int K(r)\, dh(r) = \text{Constant} < \infty , \end{aligned}$$

since

$$K(\rho)\, h(\rho) = \int_0^\rho K(\rho)\, dh(r) \leq \int_0^\rho K(r)\, dh(r) \to 0$$

as $\rho \to 0$, and similarly for the ϕ-integral.

2. A convenient geometric criterion on vanishing capacity is expressed in the following theorem.

THEOREM 2. *If the set* E *can be covered by* $A(r)$ *closed spheres of radii* $\leq r$ *and*

$$(2.1)\qquad -\int_0 \frac{K'(r)}{A(r)}\,dr = \infty\,,$$

then $C_K(E) = 0$.

Proof. We may clearly assume that all spheres have radii exactly $= r$ and that $A(r)$ denotes the lower bound. Let us assume that $C_K(E) > 0$. Then there is a mass distribution μ on E such that $I(\mu) < \infty$. We denote by $\mu(r, a)$ the mass distributed on $|x - a| \leq r$. We then find—the partial integrations can be shown to be justified as above and we assume $K \equiv 0$, $r > r_0$—

$$I(\mu) = \int d\mu(y) \int K(|x - y|)\, d\mu(x) = \int d\mu(y) \int_{r=0}^{\infty} K(r)\, d\mu(r, y) =$$

$$(2.2)\qquad = \int d\mu(y) \left[-\int \mu(r, y)\, K'(r)\, dr\right] \geq$$

$$\geq \sum_{n=0}^{\infty} \int_{2^{-n-1}}^{2^{-n}} - K'(r)\, dr \int \mu(2^{-n-1}, y)\, d\mu(y)\,.$$

Let us now assume that

$$E \subset \bigcup_{\nu=1}^{A_n} S_\nu^{(n)}\,, \qquad A_n = A(2^{-n})\,,$$

where $S_\nu^{(n)}$ are closed spheres of radii 2^{-n}. Since A_n is minimal, it is easy to see that there is a constant C, only depending on the dimension d, such that every point $P \in E$ is contained in at most C spheres. The inequality (2.2) can be continued

$$I(\mu) \geq \sum_{n=0}^{\infty} \int_{2^{-n-1}}^{2^{-n}} - K'(r)\, dr\, C^{-1} \sum_{\nu=1}^{A_{n+2}} \int_{S_\nu^{(n+2)}} \mu(2^{-n-1}, y)\, d\mu(y) \geq$$

$$\geq C^{-1} \sum_{n=0}^{\infty} \int_{2^{-n-1}}^{2^{-n}} - K'(r)\, dr \sum_{\nu=1}^{A_{n+2}} \mu(S_\nu^{(n+2)})^2 .$$

By Schwarz's inequality we have

$$\mu(E)^2 \leq \Big(\sum_{\nu=1}^{A_n} \mu(S_\nu^{(n)}) \Big)^2 \leq A_n \sum_{\nu=1}^{A_n} \mu(S_\nu^{(n)})^2 ,$$

whence

$$\sum_{n=0}^{\infty} (K(2^{-n-1}) - K(2^{-n}))\, A_{n+2}^{-1} < \infty . \tag{2.3}$$

Since clearly

$$A_n \leq A_{n+1} \leq \text{Const.}\, A_n$$

and since $A(r)$ is a decreasing function of r, the integral (2.1) and the series (2.3) converge simultaneously. We have thus got a contradiction and so $C_K(E) = 0$.

3. *Some examples.* As tests of the results obtained we now consider certain sets of the Cantor type.

THEOREM 3. *Let E be the usual d-dimensional Cantor set so that the set E_n obtained in n:th step, consists of 2nd intervals with edges of length ℓ_n. Then E has positive K-capacity if and only if*

$$\sum_{\nu} 2^{-\nu d} K(\ell_\nu) < \infty . \tag{3.1}$$

Proof. 1) Assume that (3.1) holds. Define μ_n of mass 1 with support on E_n and uniform density on E_n. Choose $x_0 \in E_n$. At a distance of $< \ell_{n-1}$ from x_0 there are at most $(4+1)^d$ intervals of E_n and at a distance $< \ell_{n-\nu}$ at most $(2 \cdot 2^\nu + 1)^d$ intervals. We find

$$\int K(|x_0 - y|)\, d\mu_n(y) \le \text{Const.}\ \{\ell_n^{-d} \int_{|t|<\ell_n} 2^{-nd} K(|t|)\, dt \; +$$

$$+ \sum_{\nu=0}^{n} 2^{(\nu-n)d} K(\ell_{n-\nu})\} \le \text{Const.}\,,$$

since

$$\ell_n^{-d} \int_{|t|<\ell_n} 2^{-nd} K(|t|)\, dt \le \ell_n^{-d}\, 2^{-nd} \sum_{\nu=n}^{\infty} \int_{\ell_{\nu+1}<|t|<\ell_\nu} K(|t|)\, dt$$

$$\le \text{Const.}\ \{K(\ell_{n+1})\, 2^{-nd} + K(\ell_{n+2}) \left(\frac{\ell_{n+1}}{\ell_n}\right)^d 2^{-nd} + \dots\} \le$$

$$\le \text{Const.} \sum_{n}^{\infty} K(\ell_\nu)\, 2^{-\nu d} \to 0\,.$$

2) For the converse, we use Theorem 2 and observe that

$$A(\ell_n) \le \text{Const.}\ 2^{nd}\,.$$

We find

$$-\int_0 \frac{K'(r)}{A(r)}\, dr = \sum^{\infty} - \int_{\ell_{n+1}}^{\ell_n} \frac{K'(r)}{A(r)}\, dr \ge$$

$$\ge \sum^{\infty} \frac{1}{A(\ell_{n+1})} (K(\ell_{n+1}) - K(\ell_n)) \ge$$

$$\ge \sum^{\infty} (K(\ell_{n+1}) - K(\ell_n)) \cdot \text{Const.}\ 2^{-nd} = \text{Const.} \sum^{\infty} K(\ell_n)\, 2^{-nd}\,.$$

Theorem 3 is now proved and we have shown that the geometric criterion in Theorem 2 is sharp. We shall now prove that the first condition of Theorem 1 also is best possible. In order to simplify the constructions we restrict ourselves to *linear* sets. The construction will be of the following generalized Cantor type.

Let $\{a_\nu\}$ and $\{b_\nu\}$ be non-increasing positive numbers such that $\Sigma\, b_\nu = \infty$. On $(0, 1)$ we construct *closed* I-intervals and *open* ω-intervals in the following way.

To the left we put $I_1^{(1)}$ of length a_1;

after $I_1^{(1)}$ we put $\omega_1^{(1)}$ of length b_1;

then follows $I_2^{(1)}$ of length a_2;

then follows $\omega_2^{(1)}$ of length b_2;

$\vdots$

then follows $I_{n_1}^{(1)}$ of length a_{n_1}.

We assume that the intervals constructed so far cover $(0, 1)$ exactly. The first approximation to the Cantor set is

$$E^{(1)} = \cup\, I_\nu^{(1)}$$

We next treat the interval $I_1^{(1)}$ in the same manner, starting with a_{n_1+1} resp. b_{n_1}. In this way we get I-intervals $I_\nu^{(2)}$, $\nu \le n_\nu^{(2)}$ and corresponding ω-intervals. We continue with $I_2^{(1)}, \ldots, I_{n_1}^{(1)}$. Together we get in this second stage $I_\nu^{(2)}$, $1 \le \nu \le n_2$, and $\omega_\nu^{(2)}$, $1 \le \nu \le n_2 - n_1$, and we form

$$E^{(2)} = \cup\, I_\nu^{(2)}.$$

It is clear how the construction proceeds and we define

$$E = \bigcap_{n=1}^{\infty} E^{(n)}$$

The potentials, to be considered, are formed as follows. Let μ_1 be the unit mass distributed uniformly on the intervals $I_\nu^{(1)}$, the mass n_1^{-1} on every such interval. The mass on $I_\nu^{(1)}$, $1 \leq \nu \leq n_1$, is redistributed on its subinterval $I_\mu^{(2)}$, uniformly and with the same total mass on every subinterval of $I_\nu^{(1)}$. The resulting set function is called μ_2. This construction is repeated and we see that $\{\mu_n\}$ converges, $\mu_n \to \mu$, and that $S_\mu \subset E$. The potential corresponding to μ_n resp. μ and the kernel under consideration are called u_n resp. u.

We shall now prove the following theorem.

THEOREM 4. *For any $K(r)$ and any measure function $h(r)$ such that*

$$\varliminf_{r \to 0} h(r)\,\overline{K}(r) = 0$$

there is a set E as above with $C_K(E) > 0$ and $M_h(E) = 0$.

Proof. Define r_ν so that

$$h(r_\nu)\,\overline{K}(r_\nu) = \varepsilon_\nu^2 \to 0. \tag{3.4}$$

We shall determine a subsequence $\{r_{\nu_i}\}$ and choose the intervals $I_\nu^{(i)}$ of length r_{ν_i} and define

$$n_i = \left[\overline{K}(r_{\nu_i})\,\varepsilon_{\nu_i}^{-1}\right].$$

(3.4) then implies $M_h(E) = 0$.

Let us now consider the potentials $u_i(x)$ and assume that

$$u_i(x) \leq M_i .$$

When discussing an upper bound for $u_{i+1}(x)$, it is by the maximum principle sufficient to consider points $x_0 \in E^{(i+1)}$. Let $x_0 \in I_\nu^{(i)} = I$. We write

$$u'_j(x_0) = \int_I K(|x_0 - y|)\, d\mu_j(y).$$

$u_{i+1}(x_0)$ and $u'_{i+1}(x_0)$ depend on $r_{\nu_{i+1}}$ and $u_{i+1}(x_0) - u'_{i+1}(x_0)$ tends uniformly (with respect to x_0 and ν) to $u_i(x_0) - u'_i(x_0)$ as $r_{\nu_{i+1}} \to 0$. For $u'_{i+1}(x_0)$ we have the estimate, if we assume that I each I has been devided into m intervals $I_\mu^{(i+1)}$ at equal distance, and each observe how μ_{i+1} is obtained from μ_i:

$$\begin{aligned} u'_{i+1}(x_0) &\leq 2m^{-1} \cdot \mu_i(I) \frac{1}{r_{\nu_{i+1}}} \int_0^{\frac{1}{2} r_{\nu_{i+1}}} K(t)\, dt + u'_i(x_0) \leq \\ &\leq \frac{\overline{K}(r_{\nu_{i+1}})}{m \cdot n_i} + u'_i(x_0) = \\ &= \frac{\overline{K}(r_{\nu_{i+1}})}{n_{i+1}} + u'_i(x_0) \leq \\ &\leq \varepsilon_{\nu_{i+1}} + u'_i(x_0). \end{aligned}$$

We can thus choose ν_{i+1} so large that for $x \in E^{(i+1)}$, e.g.,

$$u_{i+1}(x) \leq u_i(x) + 2^{-i} \leq M_i + 2^{-i}.$$

Hence the potentials $u_i(x)$ are uniformly bounded and so $C_K(E) > 0$.

The Cantor set shows that the second criterion of Theorem 1 cannot be improved. In the other direction, we shall now finally show that no complete description of capacity in terms of Hausdorff measure is possible.

THEOREM 5. *There is a set E, of the type used in Theorem 4, such that $M_h(E) = 0$ for every $h(r)$ such that*

$$\int_0 \frac{h(r)}{r}\, dr < \infty, \tag{3.5}$$

while the capacity is positive for $K(r) = \log \frac{1}{r}$.

Proof. Let us assume that $I_\nu^{(k)}$ have been constructed $1 \leq k \leq i$, $1 \leq \nu \leq n_i$, and that

$$u_k(x) \leq M_k, \quad 1 \leq k \leq i.$$

We choose numbers $m_1, \ldots, m_{n_i}$, $m_{j+1} > 2m_j$, sufficiently large. The $I^{(i+1)}$-intervals of $I_\nu^{(i)}$ are chosen of length

$$e^{-m_\nu}, e^{-m_\nu - 1}, \ldots, e^{-2m_\nu}, \tag{3.6}$$

and the ω-intervals all of length $e^{-q\nu}$. Using the notations of the proof of Theorem 4 we see that, $x_0 \in I = I_\nu^{(i)}$,

$$u_{i+1}(x_0) - u'_{i+1}(x_0) \to u_i(x_0) - u'_i(x_0), \quad m_1 \to \infty,$$

uniformly. Also

$$u'_{i+1}(x_0) \leq \frac{1}{(m_\nu + 1)} \cdot \mu_i(I) \cdot 2e^{2m_\nu} \int_0^{\frac{1}{2}e^{-2m_\nu}} \log \frac{1}{t}\, dt + u'_i(x_0) \leq$$

$$\leq 2\mu_i(I) + u'_i(x_0) + O\left(\frac{1}{m_\nu}\right).$$

Choosing $m_1, \ldots, m_{n_i}$ large enough we see as before that for given $x_0 \in E$, $\Sigma\, \mu_i(I)$ and $\Sigma \frac{1}{m_\mu}$ can be chosen uniformly bounded so that $C_K(E) > 0$, $K = \log \frac{1}{r}$. —We now observe that E can be covered by intervals of length (3.6), $\nu = 1, \ldots, n_i$ and that every exponent occurs at most in one sequence (3.6). Hence

$$M_h(E) \leq \sum_{j=m_1}^{\infty} h(e^{-j}) < \int_0^{e^{-m_1+1}} \frac{h(r)}{r} dr.$$

Hence $M_h(E) = 0$, if (3.5) holds.

4. The notion of capacity is connected with two elementary extremal problems, which historically were considered before capacities. —Let F be a compact set and define

$$(4.1) \qquad M_n = M_n(F) = \sup_{\{x_\nu\}} \inf_{x \in F} \frac{1}{n} \Sigma K(|x - x_\nu|)$$

and

$$(4.2) \qquad D_n = D_n(F) = \inf_{x_\nu \in F} \binom{n}{2}^{-1} \sum_{1 \le \nu < \mu \le n} K(|x_\nu - x_\mu|).$$

D_n is called generalized diameter (note $n = 2$) and M_n a Tscheby-scheff constant (on account of the significance of (4.1) for $d = 2$ and $K(r) = \log \frac{1}{r}$). The following theorem holds.

THEOREM 6. *If* $C_K(F) > 0$, *and* F *is compact, the limits* $\lim_{n \to \infty} M_n = M$ *and* $\lim_{n \to \infty} D_n = D$ *(transfinite diameter) exist and*

$$M^{-1} = D^{-1} = C_K(F).$$

If $C_K(F) = 0$, *then* $M_n \to \infty$ *and* $D_n \to \infty$.

Proof. We first assume $C_K(F) > 0$.

1) $D_{n+1} \le M_n$.

Since $K(r)$ is continuous, the lower bound defining D_{n+1} is actually a minimum, i.e., $\{x_\nu\}_1^{n+1}$ exist so that

$$D_{n+1} = \frac{2}{n(n+1)} \sum_{i<j} K(|x_i - x_j|) = \frac{1}{n(n+1)} \sum_{i \ne j} K(|x_i - x_j|) =$$

$$= \frac{1}{n+1} \sum_{i=1}^{n+1} \frac{1}{n} \sum_{j \ne i} K(|x_i - x_j|).$$

If $x_1, x_2, \ldots, x_{i-1}, x_{i+1}, \ldots, x_{n+1}$ are considered fixed, x_i is chosen to minimize

$$a_i(x) = \frac{1}{n} \sum_{j \neq i} K(|x - x_j|)$$

for all $x \in F$. From the definition (4.1) we see that $a_i(x_i) \leq M_n$ and from the last expression for D_{n+1} above that

$$D_{n+1} = \frac{1}{n+1} \sum_{i=1}^{n+1} a_i(x_i) \leq M_n .$$

2) $M_n \leq C_K(F)^{-1} = V$.

By definition, there is a distribution μ of unit mass on F such that

$$\int K(|x - y|)\, d\mu(y) \leq V$$

everywhere. Hence

$$\inf_{x \in F} \frac{1}{n} \sum_{\nu=1}^{n} K(|x - x_\nu|) \leq \frac{1}{n} \sum_{\nu=1}^{n} \int_F K(|x - x_\nu|)\, d\mu(x) \leq V .$$

Taking the upper bound over $\{x_\nu\}$ we get $M \leq V$.

3) $V \leq \lim_{n \to \infty} D_n$.

Define μ_n to be the mass distribution with masses n^{-1} at those points x_ν which minimize D_n. Define $K^{(N)}(r)$:

$$K^{(N)}(r) = \text{Min}\,(K(r), N) .$$

Then

$$I_{K^{(N)}}(\mu_n) \leq D_n + \frac{N}{n} .$$

Let $n \to \infty$ and choose n_ν so that $D_{n_\nu} \to \underline{\lim}\, D_{n_\nu}$ and so that $\mu_{n_\nu} \to \mu$. Then $S_\mu \subset F$ and

$$I_{K^{(N)}}(\mu) \leq \underline{\lim}\, D_n .$$

As $N \to \infty$ we obtain

$$V \leq I_K(\mu) \leq \underline{\lim}\, D_n .$$

Combining 1), 2) and 3) we now get

$$V \leq \underline{\lim}\, D_n \leq \left\{ \begin{matrix} \overline{\lim}\, D_n \\ \\ \underline{\lim}\, M_n \end{matrix} \right\} \leq \overline{\lim}\, M_n \leq V .$$

If $C(F) = 0$ choose $F' \supset F$ with $C(F') > 0$. Since

$$D_n(F) \geq D_n(F')$$

and

$$M_n(F) \geq M_n(F')$$

we find

$$\left. \begin{matrix} \underline{\lim}\, D_n(F) \\ \\ \underline{\lim}\, M_n(F) \end{matrix} \right\} \geq C_K(F')^{-1}$$

where the right hand side is arbitrarily large.

§ V. *EXISTENCE OF BOUNDARY VALUES*

1. The most famous theorem on exceptional sets is Fatou's theorem on the existence of boundary values for a function bounded and analytic in the unit circle. This result has then been generalized in different directions, and a very general version will be given in section 2. In order to make the argument clear, an outline of a proof of Fatou's theorem is given here.

Let $u(z)$ be harmonic in $|z| < 1$ and assume $u(z) \geq 0$. By the Poisson formula we have for $r < R < 1$

$$(1.1) \quad u(re^{i\theta}) = \frac{1}{2\pi} \int_{-\pi}^{\pi} \frac{R^2 - r^2}{R^2 + r^2 - 2Rr\cos(\theta - \phi)}\, u(Re^{i\phi})\, d\phi .$$

In particular,

$$(1.2) \qquad u(0) = \frac{1}{2\pi} \int_{-\pi}^{\pi} u(Re^{i\phi})\, d\phi .$$

We can thus select a sequence $R_n \to 1$ so that $u(R_n e^{i\phi})\, d\phi$ converge weakly to some non-negative measure $d\mu$. We decompose $d\mu$ by Lebesgue's theorem:

$$(1.3) \qquad d\mu = f(\phi)\, d\phi + ds(\phi) ,$$

where $s(\phi)$ is singular. Formula (1.1) becomes

$$(1.4) \qquad u(re^{i\theta}) = \int_{-\pi}^{\pi} P(r;\, \theta - \phi)\left(f(\phi)\, \frac{d\phi}{2\pi} + \frac{1}{2\pi}\, ds(\phi)\right),$$

where P is the Poisson kernel, i.e. the normal derivative of the

Green's function.

The standard way to prove that

$$(1.5) \qquad \lim u(z) \quad exists\ a.e., \qquad z \to e^{i\theta} \quad non\text{-}tang.,$$

is by means of a partial integration in (1.4) and Lebesgue's theorem on the existence of the derivative of an indefinite integral. This argument requires estimate of $\frac{\partial P}{\partial \theta}$, which makes generalizations difficult. However, using a slightly stronger version of Lebesgue's theorem we obtain a proof not depending on partial integrations and therefore possible to generalize.

It is well known that almost everywhere (θ)

$$(1.6) \qquad \int_{-t}^{t} \{|f(\theta) - f(\theta+\phi)|\, d\phi + ds(\phi)\} = o(t), \quad t \to 0.$$

We assume that (1.6) holds for $\theta = 0$ and consider for simplicity only radial approach in (1.5). Choose $\delta > 0$, fixed as $r \to 1$, and define N so that $2^N\eta \leq \delta < 2^{N+1}\eta$, $\eta = 1 - r$. From (1.4) it follows

$$|u(r) - f(0)| \leq \int_{-\eta}^{\eta} + \sum_{\nu=0}^{N} \int_{2^\nu\eta \leq |\phi| < 2^{\nu+1}\eta} |f(\phi) - f(0)|\, P\, \frac{d\phi + ds}{2\pi} +$$

$$+\ u(0) \operatorname*{Max}_{|\phi| \geq \delta} P(r,\phi) \leq$$

$$(1.7) \qquad \leq o(\eta) \operatorname{Max} P + \sum_{\nu=0}^{N} o(2^\nu\eta) \operatorname*{Max}_{2^\nu\eta \leq |\phi|} P + o(1) \leq$$

$$\leq o\left\{\sum_{\nu=0}^{N} \frac{2^\nu}{2^{2\nu}}\right\} = o(1).$$

2. We shall now use the above argument to prove a boundary value theorem for harmonic functions of several variables. The lack of the method of conformal mapping introduces technical difficulties in proofs of rather evident results. This fact is clearly illustrated in section 4.

Before stating the theorem we introduce some notations. We consider points $P = (x_1, x_2, \ldots, x_d; y) = (x; y)$ in $(d+1)$-dimensional Euclidean space. $|x|$ denotes distance on the d-dimensional subspace $X = \{P | y = 0\}$, dx denotes the volume element in X. By $V_\alpha(x^0)$ we mean the cone

$$V_\alpha(x^0) : |x - x^0| < \alpha y .$$

THEOREM 1. *Let $u(P)$ be harmonic in $y > 0$ and assume that for almost all $x \in X$, there is a cone $V_\beta(x)$ so that $u(P)$ is bounded from below in $V_\beta(x)$. Then*

$$\lim u(P),\ P \to (x; 0),\ P \in V_\alpha(x), \tag{2.1}$$

exists a.e. on X for all α.

Proof. We consider only x's belonging to some bounded set, e.g., $|x| < 1$. If we avoid an open subset O of measure $m\,O < \varepsilon$, we have for $y \leq y_0$ and a certain α independent of x, $u(P) \geq$ Const., $P \in V_\alpha(x)$, $x \notin O$. We form the region

$$R = R(O) = \{ \bigcup_{x \notin O} V_\alpha(x)\} \cap \{P \,\big|\, |x| < 1,\ y < y_0\} .$$

If y_0 is large enough R is connected. We may assume that $u \geq 0$ in R. We observe that every boundary point P of R satisfies the Poincaré condition (some cone with vertex at P is contained in the complement of R). The Dirichlet problem can thus be solved for R. Let R_n be the part of R where $y > n^{-1}$ and let $G_n(P)$ be the Green's function for R_n with some fixed pole P_0. We need a uniform estimate of $G_n(P)$.

Let $\phi(t)$ denote the distance from $t \in O$ to the complement O' of O and form

$$h(x;y) = y\int_{O} \frac{\phi(t)\,dt}{\{(t-x)^2 + y^2\}^{(d+1)/2}} = y\, h_1(x;y).$$

$h(x;y)$ is harmonic in $y > 0$. Observing that $\phi(t) \geq \frac{1}{2}\phi(x)$ if $|t-x| \leq \frac{1}{2}\phi(x)$, we see that $h(x;C\phi(x)) \geq \lambda_d C^{-d}\phi(x)$, where λ_d only depends on d. (Points with $|x| = 1$ are also easily taken care of.) This implies that $h(x;z) \geq C'_{\alpha}\cdot z$, $z = y - n^{-1}$, for $(x;y)$ on the part of ∂R_n, where $n^{-1} < y < y_0$, $|x| < 1$. Let $G_n^*(P)$ be the Green's function for the cylinder $n^{-1} < y < y_0$, $|x| < 1$, with pole at P_0. Clearly, if $\delta > 0$ is given, there exist two constants $c_1, c_2 > 0$ so that

$$c_1 z \leq G^*(P) \leq c_2 z$$

if $|x| < 1 - \delta$ and $y < \delta$ say. The second relation holds for all $|x| < 1$. By the maximum principle

$$G_n(P) \geq G^*(P) - C_\alpha h(x;z) \quad \text{in} \quad R_n.$$

Hence for $c = c(\delta)$ independent of n and $|x| < 1-\delta$, $y < \delta$,

$$G_n(P) \geq 2c(z - C_\alpha h(x;z)) = 2c\cdot z(1 - C_\alpha h_1).$$

We now need an estimate of $h_1(x;z) \leq h_1(x;0)$. We have

$$\int_{O'} h_1(x;0)\,dx \leq \int_O \phi(t)\,dt \int_{|x-t|\geq\phi(t)} \frac{dx}{|x-t|^{d+1}} \leq$$

$$\leq \lambda_d \int_O dt = \lambda_d m O < \lambda_d \varepsilon.$$

Hence $h_1(x;z) \leq (2C_\alpha)^{-1}$ for all z, except when $x \in O_1$, $m\,O_1 < 2\lambda_d C_\alpha \varepsilon = \varepsilon_1$.

What will be needed of the above investigation of G_n is that

$$\frac{\partial G_n}{\partial n} \geq c \quad \text{for all } n,\ P \in \partial R_n,\ y = n^{-1},$$

except for x in a set S of measure $< \varepsilon + \varepsilon_1$.

We now consider the harmonic measure $\omega_n(e;P)$ of a certain subset e of ∂R_n at a point $P \in R_n$. If $P = P_0$ we delete the variable P. Harnack's inequality yields

$$M(P)^{-1} \leq \frac{\omega_n(e;P)}{\omega_n(e)} \leq M(P)$$

with $M(P)$ independent of n and e, $n > n(P)$. We can write $d\omega_n(\cdot;P) = K_n(\cdot;P)\,d\omega_n$. Here $K_n(P)$ is harmonic in P and satisfies the inequality above. Also $K_n(P_0) = 1$. We form $u_\varepsilon(P) = u(x;y+\varepsilon)$ and have

(2.2) $$u_\varepsilon(P) = \int_{\partial R_n} u_\varepsilon(Q)\,K_n(Q;P)\,d\omega_n(Q).$$

This formula corresponds to (1.1). Letting $n \to \infty$ we obtain with obvious notations

$$u_\varepsilon(P) = \int_{\partial R} u_\varepsilon(Q)\,K(Q;P)\,d\omega(Q).$$

Letting $\varepsilon \to 0$ we get for a certain $f \in L^1(d\omega)$ and with s singular with respect to ω

(2.3) $$u(P) = \int_{\partial R} f(Q)\,K(Q;P)\,d\omega(Q) + \int_{\partial R} K(Q;P)\,ds(Q).$$

(2.3) is the analogue of (1.4).

3. Let us consider a point $Q_0 = (x;0) \in \partial R$ such that

(a) Q_0 is a point of density for the complement of S,

(b) $$\int_{|x|<\varepsilon} |f(Q) - f(Q_0)|\,d\omega(Q) + \int_{|x|<\varepsilon} ds(Q) = o(\varepsilon^d),\ \varepsilon \to 0,\ Q = (x_0 + x;y).$$

Since Lebesgue's theorem on symmetric derivatives holds for d dimensions, an inspection of the proof of (1.6) shows that (b) (as well as (a)) holds a.e. Namely, decompose $d\omega = \psi(Q)\,dQ + d\tau(Q)$ where $\psi \in L^1(dQ)$ and τ is singular with respect to Lebesgue measure. Then $f \in L^1(d\tau)$ and

$$\int\limits_{|x|<\varepsilon} |f(Q) - f(Q_0)|\,\psi dQ \le \int\limits_{|x|<\varepsilon} |f(Q)\,\psi(Q) - f(Q_0)\,\psi(Q_0)|\,dQ + \int\limits_{|x|<\varepsilon} f(Q_0)\,|\psi(Q) - \psi(Q_0)|\,dQ = o(\varepsilon^d)$$

almost everywhere. Since τ is singular

$$\int\limits_{|x|<\varepsilon} f(Q)\,d\tau(Q) = o(\varepsilon^d) \quad \text{a.e.}$$

We finally observe that $\dfrac{\partial G_n}{\partial n} \ge c$ for $(x;y) \in \partial R_n$, $x \notin S$. Since the surface element $d\sigma_n$ of ∂R_n also satisfies an inequality $d\sigma_n > c\,dQ$, it follows that s is singular also with respect to Lebesgue measure.

Let us assume that $Q_0 = (0;0)$ is a point, where (a) and (b) hold. We choose $A = (0;a)$, $a > 0$, and consider $u(A)$, as $a \to 0$. The general non-tangential approach is analogous. Define for a fixed $\delta > 0$

$$K_\nu = \{Q \mid Q \in \partial R,\ y < y_0,\ |x_i| < 2^\nu a\}$$

for $\nu = 0, 1, \ldots, N$, $2^N a \le \delta < 2^{N+1} a$, and

$$L_\nu = K_\nu - K_{\nu-1}, \quad \nu = 1, \ldots, N, \quad L_0 = K_0,$$

and

$$\Gamma = \partial R - K_N .$$

Formula (2.3) yields (cf. (1.7))

$$|u(A) - f(Q_0)| \leq |\int (f(Q) - f(Q_0))K(Q;A)\,d\omega(Q)| + \int K(Q;A)\,ds(Q) \leq$$

$$\leq \sum_{\nu=0}^{N} \sup_{Q \in L_\nu} K(Q;A)\,\varepsilon(\delta)\,2^{d\nu} a^d + O(1) \sup_{Q \in \Gamma} K(Q;A).$$

We must study the harmonic functions $K(Q;A)$ for $Q = Q^{(\nu)} \in L_\nu$ and consider first the case $\nu = 0$.

Since $\partial G_n / \partial n \geq c$ for $(x;y) \in \partial R_n$, $x \notin S$, it follows from condition (a) that the harmonic measure $v_0(P)$ of L_0 satisfies

(3.2)
$$v_0(P_0) \geq \gamma\, a^d,$$

where the constant γ is independent of a. We also observe that ∂R, $|x| < 1$, can be represented $y = \psi(x)$, where ψ satisfies a Lipschitz condition of order 1 and $\psi(x) = o(|x|)$, $|x| \to 0$.

We remove from R the set $|x_i| < 2a$, $y < ka$. The resulting domain is called R'. The harmonic measure of the part of $\partial R'$ with $|x_i| < 2a$ is called $v_0'(P)$. Since the harmonic measure of $\{P \mid P \in \partial R',$ $|x_i| = 2a,\ y < ka\}$ with respect to R' is smaller than the harmonic measure of the same set with respect to $y > 0$, it follows that its value at $P_0 = O(k)a^d$. Hence $v_0'(P)$ also satisfies that inequality (3.2) if k is small enough.

We set $K(Q^{(0)};A) = \mu_0$. From Harnack's inequality and the maximum principle it follows that

$$K(Q^{(0)};P) \geq \text{Const.}\ \mu_0\, v_0'(P).$$

Setting $P = P_0$ we find

(3.3)
$$\mu_0 \leq \text{Const.}\ a^{-d}.$$

We now choose $Q = Q^{(\nu)} = (x_\nu; y_\nu)$ and consider $B = (x_\nu; 2^\nu a)$, $\nu \leq N$. By (a) $\psi(x_\nu) = o(2^\nu a)$. We set $K(Q^{(\nu)};B) = \mu_\nu$ and find as above

$$\mu_\nu \leq \text{Const. } a^{-d} 2^{-d\nu} .$$

On the other hand, $K(Q^{(\nu)}; P)/\mu_\nu$ is a positive harmonic function which vanishes on $\partial R - L_\nu$ and $= 1$ for $P = B$. (In fact, one should first consider K_n; since all estimates are uniform, $n \to \infty$ causes no difficulty.) By Lemma 1 in section 4 and the maximum principle

$$K(Q^{(\nu)}; P) \leq \text{Const. } \mu_\nu \int_{(t;\, \psi(t) \in K_{\nu+1} - K_{\nu-2})} \frac{y\, dt}{\{(x-t)^2 + y^2\}^{(d+1)/2}}$$

for $P \in R$, $|P - Q^{(\nu)}| \geq \text{Const.} \cdot 2^\nu a$. Inserting $P = A$ we find

$$K(Q^{(\nu)}; A) \leq \text{Const. } 2^{-\nu} 2^{-\nu d} a^{-d} . \tag{3.4}$$

Finally, if $Q \in \Gamma$, the argument giving (3.4) can be used for $\nu = N$ giving $\sup_{Q \in \Gamma} K(Q; A) \to 0$, $a \to 0$. Inserting (3.4) in (3.1) we find $\lim_{a \to 0} u(A) = f(Q_0)$ and the theorem is proved.

4. LEMMA 1. *Let E be a subset of X in $|x| < 1$ and form for a fixed α*

$$R = \bigcup_{x \in E} V_\alpha(x) \cap \{P \mid |x| < 1, y < 1\}$$

and assume that the part Γ of ∂R with $|x| < 1$, $y < 1$ satisfies $y < \frac{1}{3}$. Let u be a positive harmonic function in R which vanishes continuously on ∂R except on the part of Γ which satisfies $|x| < \frac{1}{3}$. Then there exists a constant K, only depending on α, such that

$$u(x; y) \leq K \cdot u(0; \tfrac{1}{2}), \quad |x| = \tfrac{1}{2} . \tag{4.1}$$

Proof. By (2.2) it is sufficient to prove (4.1) when u is the harmonic measure of $\Gamma \cap \{P \mid |x - x_0| < \rho\}$ for ρ arbitrarily small and

$|x_0| < \frac{1}{3}$. To simplify the notations we choose $x_0 = 0$. The proof shows that this is no restriction. We use the notation K_i for constants only depending on α.

Suppose that $(0; y_0) \in \Gamma$ and consider the sets D_ν:

$$D_\nu = R \cap \{P \mid |x| < 2^\nu \rho, \;\; y \leq y_0 + K_1 2^\nu \rho = \eta_\nu\}, \;\; \nu = 0, 1, \ldots .$$

If K_1 is large enough the boundary of D_ν consists of three parts:

(1) a subset α_ν of Γ;

(2) a subset β_ν of the cylinder $|x| = 2^\nu \rho$;

(3) a "circle" γ_ν: $|x| < 2^\nu \rho$, $y = \eta_\nu$.

We use the notation $q_\nu = u(0; \eta_\nu)$. If K_1 is large enough it follows from Harnack's principle that

$$u(P) \leq K_2 \, q_\nu \;\text{ on } \gamma_\nu \tag{4.2}$$

and

$$q_{\nu-1} \leq K_2 \, q_\nu . \tag{4.3}$$

To be able to discuss $u(P)$ on β_ν we observe that R has the following property. If ξ is a given x-vector such that $|\xi| = 2^\nu \rho$ and $\eta(\xi) < y < \eta_\nu$ is the corresponding subset of β_ν, then $\eta_\nu - \eta(\xi) < K_3 2^\nu \rho$ and all points $(x; y)$ with $|x - \xi| < \alpha(y - \eta(\xi))$, $|x| < 1$, $y < 1$, belong to R. δ is a positive number to be determined later and we write $K_i(\delta)$ for functions of α and δ. (4.2) and the above mentioned property of R imply, again by Harnack's inequality, that

$$u(\xi; y) \leq K_4(\delta) \, q_\nu, \quad \eta(\xi) + \delta \, 2^\nu \rho < y < \eta_\nu . \tag{4.4}$$

We shall now show by induction that, for ρ small enough,

$$u(P) \leq K_5 \, q_j, \quad P \in \beta_j \cup \gamma_j . \tag{4.5}$$

Let us first consider $j = 0$. That (4.5) holds in this case is easily seen if we compare u with the harmonic measure of the bottom of a cylinder with radius ρ and side $K_6 \rho$, evaluated at its center of gravity. We now assume that (4.5) holds for $j \leq \nu - 1$. To prove (4.5) on $\beta_\nu \cup \gamma_\nu$ it is, by (4.2) and (4.4) only the part of β_ν with $\eta(\xi) < y \leq \eta(\xi) + \delta 2^\nu \rho$ that has to be considered.

Let Σ be the following auxiliary domain

$$\Sigma : P \in \Sigma \text{ if, } ay > -|x|, \ |x - (-1, 0, \ldots, 0)| > \frac{1}{2}$$

and let $\omega(P)$ be the harmonic measure of the part of $\partial\Sigma$ which is not the cone $ay = -|x|$.

We now shrink Σ by a length factor $2^{\nu+1}\rho$ and make a translation and rotation of the resulting domain to a domain with vertex of the cone at $(\xi; \eta(\xi))$ and cylinder axis along the y-axis. ω becomes ω_1 and it follows from the maximum principle, the induction assumption and (4.3) that

$$u(P) \leq K_5 \, q_{\nu-1} \, \omega_1(P) \leq K_7 \, q_\nu \, \omega_1(P)$$

in $D_\nu - D_{\nu-1}$. Since $\omega(0; y) \to 0$, $y \to 0$, it follows that

$$\omega_1(\xi; \eta(\xi) + s\, 2^\nu \rho) < \varepsilon$$

if $s < \delta(\varepsilon)$. Hence if $\delta = \delta(K_7^{-1} K_5)$, (4.5) is proved for $j = \nu$.

The induction can be continued as long as $2^\nu \rho \leq \frac{1}{2}$. The maximum principle now shows that (4.1) holds.

5. Theorem 1 is easily seen to be best possible as to the size of the exceptional set. Let E be measurable on the unit circle $(d = 2)$ of measure zero. Choose open sets $O_n \supset E$, $m\, O_n < 2^{-n}$, and define

$$u(re^{i\theta}) = \sum_{n=0}^{\infty} \frac{1}{2\pi} \int_{O_n} \frac{1 - r^2}{1 + r^2 - 2r\cos(\theta - \phi)} \, d\phi \, .$$

Then $u(0) = \Sigma\, 2^{-n}$ so u is positive and harmonic in $r < 1$ and for $\theta \in E$

$$\varliminf_{r \to 1} u(re^{i\theta}) \geq \sum_{n=0}^{N} 1 \geq N + 1 \quad \text{for all } N.$$

We shall now consider restrictions on u which guarantee a smaller exceptional set. It then turns out that, on one hand, the assertion on the existence of boundary values for *harmonic* functions can be strengthened to convergence of the corresponding Fourier series (the well-known Kolmogoroff example shows that this fails for the general Fatou theorem), while, on the other hand, the existence of boundary values holds for a general class of functions. In this section we prove the first assertion.

THEOREM 2. *Let $K(r)$ $(d = 1)$ have the properties $K(0) = \infty$ and $K(r) \equiv 0$, $r > 1$, and define*

(5.1) $$\lambda_n^{-1} = \int_0^1 K(x) \cos nx \, dx \, .$$

Then, by Lemma III.2, $\lambda_n > 0$. Consider the Fourier series

(5.2) $$\sum_1^{\infty} (a_n \cos nx + b_n \sin nx)$$

and assume

(5.3) $$\sum_1^{\infty} (a_n^2 + b_n^2)\, \lambda_n < \infty .$$

Then (5.2) converges except when x belongs to a set E such that $C_{\overline{K}}(E) = 0$, where, as before

$$\overline{K}(r) = \frac{1}{r} \int_0^r K(x)\, dx .$$

Conversely, if E is closed and $C_K(E) = 0$ and $K(x)$ satisfies $K(x) = O(K(2x))$, $x \to 0$, there is a series (5.2), satisfying (5.3), which diverges on E.

The proof depends on the following lemma.

LEMMA 2. *With the notations of Theorem 2, there is a constant M so that for all x and n, $-\pi \leq x \leq \pi$,*

$$\left| \sum_{\nu=1}^{n} \frac{\cos \nu x}{\lambda_\nu} \right| \leq M \overline{K}(|x|).$$

Proof. Define

$$k_n(x) = \frac{1}{2}\lambda_0^{-1} + \sum_{\nu=1}^{n} \frac{\cos \nu x}{\lambda_\nu} = \int_0^1 \left(\frac{1}{2} + \sum_{\nu=1}^{n} \cos \nu x \cos \nu t\right) K(t)\, dt =$$

$$= \int_0^1 (D_n(x+t) + D_n(x-t)) K(t)\, dt = I_1 + I_2$$

where $D_n(x)$ is the Dirichlet kernel

$$D_n(x) = \frac{\sin(n+\frac{1}{2})x}{4 \sin \frac{x}{2}} .$$

$D_n(x)$ satisfies the inequalities

$$|D_n(x)| < \frac{1}{4\,|\sin \frac{x}{2}|} < \frac{M_1}{|x|} \tag{5.4}$$

and

$$\left| \int_0^x D_n(t)\, dt \right| \leq M_2 . \tag{5.5}$$

We find, if $x > 0$,

$$|I_1| = \left| \int_0^1 D_n(x+t) K(t)\, dt \right| \leq \left| \int_0^x \right| + \left| \int_x^1 \right| = J_1 + J_2 .$$

Here, by the inequality (5.4),

$$J_1 \le \frac{M_1}{x} \int_0^x K(t)\,dt = M_1 \overline{K}(x)$$

and by (5.5)

$$J_2 = \left| \int_x^1 \left(\int_x^t D_n(u)\,du \right) \right| K'(t) |\,dt \le 2\,M_2\,K(x) \le 2\ M_2 \overline{K}(x).$$

I_2 is decomposed

$$I_2 = \left| \int_0^{x/2} \right| + \left| \int_{x/2}^{3x/2} \right| + \left| \int_{3x/2}^{1} \right|$$

and these terms are estimated as above.

Proof of Theorem 2. 1) We assume (5.2) given, satisfying (5.3) and form

$$q_n(x) = \sum_{\nu=1}^{n} \frac{\cos \nu x}{\sqrt{\lambda_\nu}} .$$

There are functions $F_p(x) \in L^2(-\pi, \pi)$ with Fourier series

$$F_p(x) \sim \sum_{\nu=p}^{\infty} (a_\nu \cos \nu x + b_\nu \sin \nu x)\ \sqrt{\lambda_\nu} .$$

The partial sums of the given series can be written

$$s_n(x) = \frac{1}{\pi} \int_{-\pi}^{\pi} F_1(t)\ q_n(x-t)\,dt .$$

Let $n(x)$ be an arbitrary Borel-measurable function, $n(x) \le N$, taking integer values and let μ be a distribution of mass on $(-\pi, \pi)$. Then

$$\left(\int_{-\pi}^{\pi} s_{n(x)}(x)\,d\mu(x) \right)^2 = \left[\frac{1}{\pi} \int_{-\pi}^{\pi} F_1(t) \left(\int_{-\pi}^{\pi} q_{n(x)}(x-t)\,d\mu(x) \right) dt \right]^2 \le$$

$$\leq \frac{1}{\pi} \int_{-\pi}^{\pi} F_1(t)^2 dt \iint_{-\pi}^{\pi} d\mu(x) d\mu(y) \frac{1}{\pi} \int_{-\pi}^{\pi} q_{n(x)}(x-t) \cdot q_{n(y)}(y-t) dt =$$

$$= \|F_1\|^2 \iint_{-\pi}^{\pi} k_{n(x,y)}(x-y)\, d\mu(x)\, d\mu(y) ,$$

where $n(x, y) = \text{Min}\,(n(x), n(y))$. Lemma 2 yields

$$(5.6) \quad \left(\int_{-\pi}^{\pi} s_{n(x)}(x)\, d\mu(x) \right)^2 \leq M \|F_1\|^2 \iint \overline{K}(|x-y|)\, d\mu(x)\, d\mu(y) .$$

Let A be a closed set where $\overline{\lim}\, s_n(x) \geq a$. Choosing μ to be the equilibrium distribution of A of mass 1 and $n(x)$ appropriately, (5.6) yields

$$(5.7) \qquad C_{\overline{K}}(A) \leq M \|F_1\|^2 a^{-2} .$$

The set E where $\overline{\lim}\, s_n(x) - \underline{\lim}\, s_n(x) \geq a > 0$ does not depend on the first p Fourier coefficients. We can thus, if $A \subset E$, replace $\|F_1\|$ by any $\|F_p\|$ and (5.7) yields $C_{\overline{K}}(A) = 0$. This proves Theorem 2,1).

2) Assume E closed with $C_K(E) = 0$. Then a finite sum of intervals F with $C_K(F) = \varepsilon$ exists for any $\varepsilon > 0$ and a distribution of mass ε on F such that

$$u(x) = \int_F K(|x-y|)\, d\mu(y) \equiv 1$$

on F and

$$I(\mu) = \iint K(|x-y|)\, d\mu(x)\, d\mu(y) = \varepsilon ,$$

while $E \subset$ interior of F. We assume $E \subset (0, 1)$ and define μ and u periodically (2π). If disregarding $\nu = 0$,

$$d\mu \sim \Sigma\, (a_\nu \cos \nu x + \beta_\nu \sin \nu x)$$

then

$$u(x) \sim \Sigma\,(\alpha_\nu \cos \nu x + \beta_\nu \sin \nu x)\,\lambda_\nu^{-1}$$
$$\sim \Sigma\,(a_\nu \cos \nu x + b_\nu \sin \nu x)$$

and

$$I(\mu) = \Sigma\,(\alpha_\nu^2 + \beta_\nu^2)\,\lambda_\nu^{-1} = \Sigma\,(a_\nu^2 + b_\nu^2)\,\lambda_\nu .$$

We now choose $F^{(1)} \supset F^{(2)} \supset \ldots \supset E$ so that $C_K(F^{(n)}) = \varepsilon_n < 2^{-n}$. Corresponding u's and μ's are also denoted with upper indices. For a sequence of integers $\{n_i\}$ to be determined later we define

$$u(x) = \Sigma\, u^{(n_i)}(x) \sim \Sigma\,(a_\nu \cos \nu x + b_\nu \sin \nu x)$$

and

$$\mu = \mu^{(n_i)} .$$

We have

$$I(\mu) < 2 \sum_{i \le j} I(\mu^{(i)}, \mu^{(j)}) \le 2 \sum_1^\infty i\,\varepsilon_i < 4 .$$

We have $\sum_{i=1}^{j} u^{(n_i)}(x) \equiv j$ on a neighbourhood of E. We assume that for the partial sums $s_k^{(j)}(x)$ of the Fourier series of $\sum_1^j u^{(n_i)}(x)$, it is true that $s_k^{(j)}(x) > j-1$ for $k \ge N_j$ and $x \in F^{(n_j)}$. If we now choose n_{j+1} large, $u^{(n_{j+1})}(x)$ influences the Fourier coefficients of $\sum_1^{j+1} u^{(n_i)}(x)$ of order $\le N_j$ arbitrarily little, while on the other hand we have $s_k^{(j+1)}(x) > j$ for $k \ge N_{j+1}$ and $x \in F^{(n_{j+1})}$. If the sequence $\{n_i\}$ is determined successively in this manner, the function u is an example of the desired kind.

6. We shall now restrict ourselves to capacities with respect to $r^{-\alpha}$

and $\log \frac{1}{r}$ and use the notations $C_\alpha(E)$ and $C_0(E)$. The following general theorem on existence of radial limits will be proved.

THEOREM 3. *Let* $f(z)$ *be continuous in* $|z| < 1$, $z = x + iy$, *having first partial derivatives a.e. in* $|z| < 1$ *such that*

$$\iint_{|x| < 1} |\text{grad } f|^2 (1 - |z|)^\alpha \, dx \, dy < \infty, \quad 0 \leq \alpha < 1, \tag{6.1}$$

and of class BL, *i.e., such that* $f(re^{i\theta})$ *is absolutely continuous for almost all* r *as a function of* θ *and for almost all* θ *as a function of* r. *Then*

$$\lim_{r \to 1} f(re^{i\theta}) = f(\theta)$$

exists except on a set E, $C_\alpha(E) = 0$.

For the proof we need some lemmas.

LEMMA 3. *Let* $q(\zeta)$ *be Borel-measurable on* $|\zeta| < 1$ *and assume*

$$\|q\|^2 = \iint_{|\zeta| < 1} |q(\zeta)|^2 d\xi \, d\eta < \infty, \quad \zeta = \xi + i\eta.$$

Let A *be the subset of* $|z| < 1$ *where*

$$Q(z) = \iint_{|\zeta| < 1} \frac{|q(\zeta)|}{|z - \zeta|} \, d\xi \, d\eta > a.$$

Then for a fixed constant C,

$$C_0(A) < C \frac{\|q\|^2}{a^2}. \tag{6.2}$$

Proof. Let μ be a distribution of unit mass on a subset A_1 of A of diameter $\leq \frac{1}{3}$.

$$a^2 < \left(\int_{A_1} Q(z)\, d\mu(z) \right)^2 \le \|q\|^2 \iint_{A_1 A_1} d\mu(z_1)\, d\mu(z_2) \iint_{|\zeta|<1} \frac{d\xi\, d\eta}{|z_1 - \zeta|\, |z_2 - \zeta|} .$$

It is easy to see that

$$(6.3) \qquad \iint_{|\zeta|<1} \frac{d\xi\, d\eta}{|z_1 - \zeta|\, |z_2 - \zeta|} < C_1 \log \frac{1}{|z_1 - z_2|} ,$$

which yields

$$(6.4) \qquad C_0(A_1) < C_1 \frac{\|q\|^2}{a^2} .$$

Adding a bounded number of inequalities (6.4), we get (6.2).

LEMMA 4. *Let* $\zeta_\nu = \rho_\nu e^{i\theta_\nu}$, $\nu = 1, 2$, *satisfy* $\frac{1}{2} < \rho_\nu < 1$. *Then for a fixed constant* $C = C_\alpha$, *depending only on* α

$$(6.5) \qquad \iint_{|z|<1} \frac{dx\, dy}{(1-|z|)^\alpha |z - \zeta_1|\, |z - \zeta_2|} \le C \begin{cases} |e^{i\theta_1} - e^{i\theta_2}|^{-\alpha}, & 0 < \alpha < 1 \\ \log \dfrac{3}{|e^{i\theta_1} - e^{i\theta_2}|} , & \alpha = 0 . \end{cases}$$

Proof. The inequality for $\alpha = 0$ is equivalent to (6.3) and we shall in the proof assume $0 < \alpha < 1$.

Mapping $|z| < 1$ conformally (or even only with bounded dilatation in both directions in the considered range) onto a half plane, we see that we may replace (6.5) by

$$H(\zeta_1, \zeta_2) = \int_0^\infty \int_{-\infty}^\infty \frac{dx\, dy}{y^\alpha |z - \zeta_1|\, |z - \zeta_2|} , \quad z = x + iy ,$$

where $\zeta_\nu = \xi_\nu + i\eta_\nu$ and $0 < \eta_1 \le \eta_2$. H is then a decreasing function of η_2, $\eta_1 \le \eta_2 < \infty$. We can thus assume $\eta_1 = \eta_2 = \eta$. For ξ_1 and ξ_2 fixed, H is a decreasing function of $\eta > 0$, whence we can assume $\eta_1 = \eta_2 = 0$. H then depends on $|\xi_1 - \xi_2|$ only and we put

$\xi_2 = 0$ and $\xi_1 = \xi > 0$. We now have

$$H = \int_0^\infty \frac{dy}{y^\alpha} \int_{-\infty}^0 \frac{dx}{|z|\,|z-\xi|} = \int_0^\infty \frac{dy}{y^\alpha} I(y, \xi).$$

In the integral I we distinguish two cases.

1) $y \geq \xi$.

$$I(y, \xi) \leq 2\int_{-\infty}^\infty \frac{dx}{|z|^2} + \int_0^{2\xi} \frac{dx}{y^2} = \frac{\pi}{y} + \frac{2\xi}{y^2}.$$

2) $y \leq \xi$.

$$I(y, \xi) \leq 2\int_{-\infty}^{-\xi} \frac{dx}{x^2} + 2\int_{-\xi}^{\xi/2} \frac{dx}{\sqrt{x^2+y^2}} \cdot \frac{2}{\xi} <$$

$$< \frac{2}{\xi} + \frac{8\sqrt{2}}{\xi} \int_0^\xi \frac{dx}{x+y} = \frac{2}{\xi} + \frac{8\sqrt{2}}{\xi} \log \frac{\xi + y}{y}.$$

The contribution H_1 to H from the estimate 1) is majorized

$$H_1 < 2\pi \int_\xi^\infty \frac{dy}{y^{1+\alpha}} + \xi \int_\xi^\infty \frac{dy}{y^{2+\alpha}} = C' \xi^{-\alpha}$$

and the analogous quantity H_2 satisfies the inequality

$$H_2 < \frac{2}{\xi} \int_0^\xi \frac{dy}{y^\alpha} + \frac{8\sqrt{2}}{\xi} \int_\xi^\infty \frac{1}{y^\alpha} \log \frac{y+\xi}{y}\, dy < C'' \xi^{-\alpha}$$

as a partial integration shows.

LEMMA 5. *Suppose that* $a(t)$, $0 \leq t \leq 1$, *satisfies the conditions*

$$a(t) \text{ absolutely continuous}, \quad a'(t) \in L^2(0, 1), \quad a(0) = 0.$$

Then for $0 \leq \alpha < 1$, *there is a constant* C *only depending on* α, *such that for any* $n \geq 1$

$$(6.6)\qquad \int_0^1 (|a'(t)|^2 + n^2|a(t)|^2)(1-t)^\alpha dt \geq C\, n^{1-\alpha}|a(1)|^2 .$$

Proof. Let τ be the largest number such that

$$|a(\tau)| = \frac{1}{2}|a(1)| .$$

Such a number clearly exists since $a(0) = 0$ and $\tau < 1$, except in the case when $a(1) = 0$. We find

$$\int_0^1 (|a'|^2 + n^2|a|^2)(1-t)^\alpha dt \geq \int_\tau^1 |a'|^2(1-t)^\alpha dt + \frac{1}{4} n^2|a(1)|^2 \int_\tau^1 (1-t)^\alpha dt \geq$$

$$\geq \Big(\int_\tau^1 |a'|dt\Big)^2 \Big(\int_\tau^1 (1-t)^{-\alpha} dt\Big)^{-1} + \frac{1}{4}(1+\alpha)^{-1} n^2|a(1)|^2 \cdot (1-t)^{1+\alpha} \geq$$

$$\geq \frac{|a(1)|^2}{4}\left\{\frac{1-\alpha}{(1-\tau)^{1-\alpha}} + \frac{n^2}{1+\alpha}(1-\tau)^{1+\alpha}\right\}.$$

Minimizing the last expression as a function of $(1-\tau)$ we obtain (6.6).

Proof of Theorem 3. We first assume that f_x and f_y are continuous in $|z| \leq \rho < 1$. We apply Green's formula to $f(z)$ and $(z-\zeta)^{-1}$ in $|z| \leq \rho$, $|z-\zeta| \geq \varepsilon$ for a fixed ζ in $|\zeta| < \rho$ and let $\varepsilon \to 0$. We get, using the notation $f_{\bar z} = \frac{1}{2}(f_x + if_y)$,

$$(6.7)\qquad f(\zeta) = \frac{1}{2\pi i}\int_{|z|=\rho} \frac{f(z)}{z-\zeta}\,dz + \frac{1}{\pi}\iint_{|z|\leq\rho} \frac{f_{\bar z}}{z-\zeta}\,dx\,dy .$$

To obtain (6.7) in the general case, choose f_n with continuous first derivatives so that

$$\iint_{|z|\leq\rho} |\mathrm{grad}\,(f_n - f)|^2 dx\,dy = \varepsilon_n \to 0,\quad n\to\infty,$$

and so that $f_n(z) \to f(z)$ uniformly in $|z| \leq \rho$. (6.7) holds for f_n and the left hand side and the first term to the right clearly tend to the corresponding expressions for f, uniformly in $|\zeta| \leq \rho' < \rho$. Let A_n be the set in $|\zeta| \leq \rho$ where

$$\left| \iint\limits_{|z| \leq \rho} \frac{f_{\bar{z}}}{z-\zeta}\, dx\, dy - \iint\limits_{|z| \leq \rho} \frac{f_{n\bar{z}}}{z-\zeta}\, dx\, dy \right| > a_n .$$

By Lemma 3 we have

$$C_0(A_n) < C\, \varepsilon_n a_n^{-2} .$$

Choosing $\varepsilon_n \to 0$, $a_n \to 0$ so that $\Sigma\, \varepsilon_n a_n^{-2} < \infty$ we see that (6.7) *holds for the given function* f *except for* ζ *on a set* E_ρ *such that* $C_0(E_\rho) = 0$.

We now study (6.7) as $\rho \to 1$ and expand the first term to the right:

$$\frac{1}{2\pi i} \int\limits_{|z| = \rho} \frac{f(z)}{z-\zeta}\, dz = \frac{1}{2\pi} \int_{-\pi}^{\pi} \frac{f(\rho e^{i\theta})}{1-\zeta z^{-1}}\, d\theta = [z = \rho e^{i\theta}]$$

$$(6.8) \qquad = \sum_{n=0}^{\infty} \zeta^n \rho^{-n} \frac{1}{2\pi} \int_{-\pi}^{\pi} f(\rho e^{i\theta}) e^{-in\theta} d\theta =$$

$$= \sum_{n=0}^{\infty} \zeta^n \rho^{-n} a_n(\rho),$$

where

$$a_n(\rho) = \frac{1}{2\pi} \int_{-\pi}^{\pi} f(\rho e^{-i\theta}) e^{-in\theta} d\theta, \quad n = 0, \pm 1, \pm 2, \ldots .$$

This yields formally

$$a_n'(\rho) = \frac{1}{2\pi} \int_{-\pi}^{\pi} f_\rho(\rho e^{i\theta}) e^{-in\theta} d\theta$$

and

$$in\, a_n(\rho) = \frac{1}{2\pi} \int_{-\pi}^{\pi} f_\theta(\rho e^{i\theta}) e^{-in\theta} d\theta,$$

which then by assumption on absolute continuity holds for almost all ρ. By (6.1) and Parseval's relation we have

$$\sum_{n=-\infty}^{\infty} \int_0^1 (|a_n'(\rho)|^2 + n^2 |a_n(\rho)|^2)(1-\rho)^\alpha d\rho < \infty ,$$

if we e.g. assume $f \equiv 0$ for $|z| < \frac{1}{2}$. By Lemma 5 there is a constant C so that for any $R < 1$

$$\sum_{n=0}^{\infty} |a_n(R)|^2 n^{1-\alpha} \leq C .$$

Choosing $R_\nu \nearrow 1$ so that $\lim_{\nu \to \infty} a_n(R_\nu) = a_n$ exist for $n \geq 0$ we find

$$\text{(6.9)} \qquad \sum_{n=0}^{\infty} |a_n|^2 n^{1-\alpha} \leq C$$

and

$$\text{(6.10)} \quad g(\zeta) = \lim_{\nu \to \infty} \frac{1}{2\pi i} \int_{|z| = R_\nu} \frac{f(z)}{z-\zeta} dz = \sum_{n=0}^{\infty} a_n \zeta^n , \quad |\zeta| < 1 .$$

We now choose $\rho = R_\nu$ in (6.7) and assume $\zeta \notin E$,

$$E = \bigcup_{\nu=1}^{\infty} E_{R_\nu} ,$$

so that $C_0(E) = 0$. Then

$$\text{(6.11)} \qquad f(\zeta) = g(\zeta) + \frac{1}{\pi} \iint_{|z|<1} \frac{f_{\bar{z}}}{z-\zeta} dx\, dy , \quad \zeta \notin E .$$

By Theorem 2, $g(\zeta)$ has radial limits except on a set of α-capacity zero. The exceptional set E where (6.11) does not hold is situated on radii corresponding to arguments belonging to a set of vanishing 0-capacity. Since such a set a fortiori has vanishing α-capacity, it is now sufficient to prove that the second term of (6.11) has radial limits except on a set of α-capacity zero.

Assume then that these limits do not exist on G, $C_\alpha(G) > 0$. To any choice of $R < 1$, $\rho(\theta)$ must exist so that for $\theta \in G_R \subset G$, $C_\alpha(G_R) \geq \frac{1}{2} C_\alpha(G)$, $\rho(\theta)$ is Borel measurable, $R < \rho(\theta) < 1$ and

$$\iint_{R<|z|<1} \frac{q(z)}{|z-\rho(\theta)e^{i\theta}|}\, dx\, dy \geq c_0 > 0, \tag{6.12}$$

where $q = |\text{grad } f|$ and c_0 is independent of R and of $\theta \in G_R$. There is a distribution μ_R of unit mass on G_R with a uniformly bounded α-potential. We integrate (6.12) with respect to μ_R and use Schwarz's inequality. We find

$$c_0^2 \leq \iint_{R<|z|<1} |q|^2 (1-|z|)^\alpha dx\, dy$$

$$\times \iint_{G_R\, G_R} d\mu_R(\theta_1)\, d\mu_R(\theta_2) \iint_{R<|z|<1} \frac{dx\, dy}{(1-|z|)^\alpha |z-\zeta_1|\, |z-\zeta_2|}$$

if $\zeta_\nu = \rho(\theta_\nu)\, e^{i\theta_\nu}$, $\nu = 1, 2$. The first factor $= \delta_R \to 0$, $R \to 1$. In the second we use Lemma 4 and find

$$c_0^2 \leq \delta_R\, C\, I(\mu_R).$$

As $R \to 1$, this implies $I(\mu_R) \to \infty$, or $C_\alpha(G_R) \to 0$, contradicting the assumption on G_R. —Theorem 3 is thus proved.

7. Theorem 3 can be used to prove the following boundary value theorem for meromorphic functions.

THEOREM 4. *Let $f(z)$ be meromorphic in $|z| < 1$ and assume*

$$\iint_{|z|<1} \frac{|f'(z)|^2}{(1+|f(z)|^2)^2} (1-|z|)^\alpha dx\, dy < \infty, \quad 0 \leq \alpha < 1. \tag{7.1}$$

Then

$$\lim f(z), \qquad z \to e^{i\theta} \textit{ non-tangentially,}$$

exists, except when θ *belongs to a set of* α*-capacity zero.*

Remark. The existence of non-tangential limits cannot be asserted for general functions. —There exists a function $\phi_\varepsilon(z)$ of class BL such that

(a) $\phi_\varepsilon(0) = 1$;

(b) $\phi_\varepsilon \equiv 0$, $|z| > \varepsilon$;

(c) $\iint |\text{grad}\, \phi_\varepsilon|^2 dx\, dy < \varepsilon$.

Choosing $z_{\nu n}$ on $|z| = 1 - 2^{-n}$ sufficiently dense and $\varepsilon_{\nu n}$ small enough

$$f(z) = \sum_{\nu, n} \phi_{\varepsilon_{\nu n}}(z - z_{\nu n})$$

is an example of the desired kind.

Proof. The proof consists of two steps.

1) We first observe that

$$\lim_{r \to 1} f(re^{i\theta}) \tag{7.2}$$

exists outside a set of α-capacity zero. This follows immediately from Theorem 3 since $(1 + |f|^2)^{-1}$ satisfies the assumptions of this theorem. Hence

$$\lim |f(re^{i\theta})| \text{ exists (possibly } = \infty) \text{ p.p. } (\alpha).$$

Replacing f by $f - c$, we see that also

$$\lim |f(re^{i\theta}) - c| \text{ exists p.p. } (\alpha).$$

Since the circles $|w| = a$ and $|w - c| = b$ intersect at most in two points and the clusterset of $f(re^{i\theta})$ must be one point or a continuum

(7.2) exists if both the above limits exist, that is except in a set of α-capacity zero.

2) To prove the existence of *non-tangential* limits we consider the circles

$$C_n: \quad |z| = 1 - 2^{-n} = r_n .$$

We choose a (large) integer a, which will determine the size of the angle, and subdivide C_n into (overlapping) sectors

$$\omega_{\nu n}: \quad \nu \cdot 2\pi \cdot 2^{-n} < \theta < \nu \cdot 2\pi \cdot 2^{-n} + 2\pi a\, 2^{-n}, \; \nu = 1, \ldots, 2^n,$$

and consider the domains

$$A_{\nu n}: \begin{cases} \theta \in \omega_{\nu n} \\ r_{n-1} < r < r_{n+2} . \end{cases}$$

If we define

$$(7.3) \qquad a_n = \sum_{\nu=1}^{2^n} \iint_{A_{\nu n}} \frac{|f'(z)|^2}{(1+|f(z)|^2)^2}\, dx\, dy \cdot 2^{-n\alpha},$$

(7.1) implies

$$\sum_1^\infty a_n = M(a) < \infty .$$

The regions $A_{\nu n}$ are divided into two groups. Assume first that

$$\iint_{A_{\nu n}} \frac{|f'(z)|^2}{(1+|f(z)|^2)^2}\, dx\, dy > 1 .$$

This holds for $m = m_n$ indices ν and by (7.3) $m < 2^{n\alpha} a_n$. We call the corresponding ω-intervals γ_{in}, $1 \leq i \leq m$, and denote their lengths $|\gamma_{in}|$. Then

$$\sum_{n=1}^{\infty} \sum_{\nu=1}^{m_n} |\gamma_{in}|^{\alpha} \leq (2\pi a)^{\alpha} \sum m_n 2^{-n\alpha} < (2\pi a)^{\alpha} \sum_{1}^{\infty} a_n < \infty .$$

If E_a denotes the set of θ's, included in infinitely many intervals γ_{in} the above inequality implies

$$\Lambda_{r^{\alpha}}(E_a) = 0$$

which then yields

$$C_{\alpha}(E_a) = 0 .$$

If we let a assume the values $1, 2, \ldots$, and set $E = \bigcup_{a=1}^{\infty} E_a$, also $C_{\alpha}(E) = 0$.

We now choose a point $\theta_0 \notin E$ where (7.2) exists and assume e.g. that the limit $= 0$. We fix an integer a. For $n \geq n_0$ this point θ_0 belongs to intervals $\omega_{\nu n}$ of the second group. This means that there are regions A_n

$$A_n : \begin{cases} |\theta - \theta_0| < 2a\, 2^{-n} \\ r_{n-1} < r < r_{n+2} \end{cases}$$

such that

$$\iint_{A_n} \frac{|f'(z)|^2}{(1+|f(z)|^2)^2}\, dx\, dy \leq 1 .$$

Since the Riemann half sphere has area $\frac{\pi}{2} > 1{,}5$, $f(z)$ omits for $z \in A_n$ a set S_n in $|w| < 1$ of area $> 0{,}5$. Let us now consider the class of measurable functions on S_n satisfying $|q(w)| \leq 1$ and form the holomorphic function in A_n

$$F_q(z) = \iint_{S_n} \frac{q(w)\, du\, dv}{f(z) - w}, \quad w = u + iv .$$

Uniformly in q *and* n, $F_q(z)$ has the following properties:

$$(7.4) \qquad |F_q(z)| \leq \text{Const.}, \quad z \in A_n$$

and

$$(7.5) \qquad \left| F_q(re^{i\theta_0}) - \iint\limits_{S_n} \frac{q(w)\,du\,dv}{-w} \right| \leq \varepsilon_n, \quad r_{n-1} < r < r_{n+2},$$

where $\varepsilon_n \to 0$ since $\lim f(re^{i\theta_0}) = 0$. By the principle of the harmonic majorant (7.4) and (7.5) imply

$$(7.6) \qquad \left| F_q(z) - \iint \frac{q(w)\,du\,dv}{-w} \right| \leq \varepsilon'_n, \quad |\theta - \theta_0| \leq a \cdot 2^{-n}, \quad r_n \leq r \leq r_{n+1},$$

where $\varepsilon'_n \to 0$, $n \to \infty$. Taking the upper bound in (7.6) for all q, $|q| \leq 1$, we get

$$\varepsilon'_n \geq \sup_{|q| \leq 1} \left| \iint\limits_{S_n} \left(\frac{1}{f(z) - w} + \frac{1}{w} \right) q(w)\,du\,dv \right| =$$

$$= \iint\limits_{S_n} \frac{|f(z)|}{|f(z) - w|\,|w|}\,du\,dv$$

which implies

$$\lim |f(z)| = 0, \quad \begin{cases} |\theta - \theta_0| \leq a \cdot 2^{-n} \\ 2^{-n} \leq 1 - r \leq 2^{-n-1}. \end{cases}$$

Since a is arbitrarily large, the theorem is proved.

We finally note that in case $a = 0$ the proof is simplified since the first case does not occur.

8. We shall, in passing, give a geometric application of Theorem 3.

THEOREM 5. *Let $f(z)$ be a differentiable mapping of $|z| < 1$ onto a surface Y over a sphere S. Let E be a totally disconnected subset of S and assume that the part of Y situated over every compact subset of $S - E$ has finite area. Then $\lim_{r \to 1} f(re^{i\theta})$ exists except on a set of logarithmic capacity zero.*

Proof. Consider an arbitrary open spherical cap K, $\overline{K} \subset S - E$. Let $\phi(s)$ be defined on S such that $\phi \equiv 0$ outside K, $\phi > 0$ on K and let ϕ have continuous derivatives. The function $\phi(f(z))$ has a finite Dirichlet integral over $|z| < 1$ by our assumptions on f. By Theorem 3, $\phi(f(z))$ then has radial limits except on a set of logarithmic capacity zero (= p.p.). The cluster set of $f(re^{i\theta})$ along a radius for which $\phi(f)$ has limits, must be a subset of $\{s \mid \phi(s) = \lambda\}$ for some λ. If $\lambda > 0$ we study another function ϕ_1 so that $\phi = \lambda > 0$ and $\phi_1 = \lambda_1 > 0$ intersect in isolated points. We thus find that p.p. either

$$\lim f(re^{i\theta}) \text{ exists}$$

or

$$\text{the cluster set of } f(re^{i\theta}) \text{ is outside } K.$$

We now cover $S - E$ by caps $\{K_\nu\}_1^\infty$ and find that the above alternative holds with K replaced by $S - E$. The second alternative now means that the cluster set is a subset of E. Since E is totally disconnected the cluster set reduces to one point, i.e.,

$$\lim f(re^{i\theta}) \text{ exists.}$$

9. It is possible to generalize Fatou's theorem in another direction. Theorem 2 gives better information about convergence of Fourier series than the classical Kolmogorov-Seliverstov-Plessner on a.e. convergence if $\lambda_n = (\log n)^{1+\delta}$, $\delta > 0$. For $\delta = 0$, however, $\overline{K}(r)$ is not integrable and Theorem 2 is empty. We can, however, consider existence of radial limits and here it is actually possible to get a complete description of the exceptional sets even in the interval $-1 < \delta < 0$. The suitable tool turns out to be the maximal functions.

Let $f(x)$ be periodic with period 2π and assume $f(x) \in L^p(-\pi, \pi)$, some $p \geq 1$. The maximal function $f^*(x)$ associated with $f(x)$ was introduced by Hardy and Littlewood through the definition

$$f^*(x) = \sup_t \frac{1}{t} \int_x^{x+t} f(u)du. \tag{9.1}$$

The inequalities

$$\int_{-\pi}^{\pi} |f^*(x)|^p dx \leq A_p \int_{-\pi}^{\pi} |f(x)|^p dx, \quad p > 1 \tag{9.2}$$

and

$$m\{x \mid f^*(x) \geq \lambda\} \leq \frac{A}{\lambda} \int_{-\pi}^{\pi} |f(x)|\, dx \tag{9.3}$$

are basic in the theory of differentiation. They can alternatively be given as theorems on harmonic functions. Assume $f > 0$ and let $u(z)$ be harmonic in $|z| < 1$ with boundary values $f(\theta)$. Then clearly

$$\text{Const. } f^*(\theta) \leq \sup_r u(re^{i\theta}) \leq \text{Const. } f^*(\theta). \tag{9.4}$$

The inequality (9.2) follows if we can characterize those non-negative measures μ for which

$$\iint_{|z|<1} u(z)^p d\mu(z) \leq A_p \int_{-\pi}^{\pi} f(x)^p dx. \tag{9.5}$$

It is sufficient to consider $p = 2$ and the complete solution is as follows: a necessary and sufficient condition on μ, is $\mu(S) \leq \text{Const.}\, s$ for every set S: $1-s < |z| < 1$, $|\arg(z) - \alpha| < s$.

The corresponding linear problem, i.e. to describe those μ for which

$$\iint u(z)\, d\mu(z) \tag{9.6}$$

is bounded for $f \in L^p$ is clearly much simpler and the solution is that

$$\phi(\theta) = \iint \frac{1-|z|^2}{|e^{i\theta} - z|^2}\, d\mu(z) \tag{9.7}$$

belongs to L^q. A solution of this problem is in principle sufficient in order to obtain results on existence of boundary values.

We shall now consider the corresponding linear problem for the class of functions $f(x)$,

$$f(x) \sim \sum_{-\infty}^{\infty} C_n e^{inx},$$

such that

$$\|f\|_K^2 = \Sigma\, |C_n|^2 \lambda_{|n|} < \infty .$$

Here $\{\lambda_n\}$ is a positive sequence such that

$$K(x) \sim \sum_0^{\infty} \frac{\cos nx}{\lambda_n}$$

is a convex function $\in L^1$. The following theorem is quite easy to prove.

THEOREM 6. *If* $\lambda_n = (n+1)^{1-\alpha}$, $0 \leq \alpha < 1$, *(9.6) is bounded if and only if*

$$E_\alpha(\mu) = \iint \frac{d\mu(a)\, d\mu(b)}{|1 - a\bar{b}|^\alpha} < \infty, \quad 0 < \alpha < 1,$$

$$E_0(\mu) = \iint \log \left| \frac{1}{1-\bar{a}\, b} \right| d\mu(a)\, d\mu(b) < \infty, \quad \alpha = 0.$$

The bound of (9.6) is $\leq$ Const. $\sqrt{E_\alpha}$.

If we specialize $d\mu$ to have the form $d\sigma(\theta)$ placed at a point on the radius from 0 to $e^{i\theta}$ we find using (9.4) and observing that $E_\alpha(\mu)$ essentially increases if we push the masses out to $|z| = 1$

$$\left(\int f^*(x)\, d\sigma(x) \right)^2 \leq A_\alpha \, \|f\|_K^2 \, I_\alpha(\sigma) \tag{9.8}$$

where I_α is the energy of σ with respect to the kernel $|x|^{-\alpha}$, resp. $\log \frac{1}{|x|}$. This inequality implies the existence of derivatives and boundary values except on sets of capacity zero, as also follows from 2.

We give the proof of Theorem 6 only in the case $\alpha = 0$ which is particularly simple. Consider first the case when μ has its support strictly inside $|z| < 1$. Consider the harmonic function

$$u_0(z) = \iint \log |1 - z\bar{\zeta}|\, d\mu(\zeta)$$

and let (u, v) denote scalar product in the space of harmonic functions with finite Dirichlet integral and with $u(0) = 0$. Then by Poisson's formula

$$(u, u_0) = \int_{|z|=1} u \frac{\partial u_0}{\partial n}\, ds = 2\pi\, u(z)\, d\mu(z).$$

Hence

$$2\pi \left| \iint u\, d\mu \right| \leq \|u_0\| \cdot \|u\|$$

with equality if $u = u_0$, and the linear functional (9.6) has norm $(2\pi)^{-1/2} \sqrt{E_0(\mu)}$. The case of a general μ follows immediately. If $u(0) = \frac{1}{2\pi} \int f dx \neq 0$, we simply consider $u - u(0)$.

10. It is clearly possible to use the same method for general kernels $K(x)$ and corresponding weights λ_n. However, the formulas become so involved that they cannot be used to deduce inequalities of the form (9.8). The case

$$\lambda_n = (\log(n+2))^a, \qquad 0 < a < \infty,$$

is particularly interesting. The kernel K_a that is associated with this sequence is

$$K_a(x) \sim \frac{1}{|x|\,(\log\frac{1}{|x|})^{1+a}}, \qquad x \to 0.$$

The following theorem holds.

THEOREM 7. *There is a constant B_a such that*

$$C_{K_a}\,[\{x \mid f^*(x) \geq \lambda\}] \leq \frac{B_a}{\lambda^2}\,\|f\|^2_{K_a}, \quad 0 < a < \infty.$$

Remark. By standard methods this implies that the primitive function of f has a derivative and that the corresponding harmonic function has boundary values except on sets of K_a-capacity zero.

In the proof we use the equivalent norm

$$(10.1) \qquad \iint_{-\pi}^{\pi} \frac{|f(x)-f(y)|^2}{\phi(x-y)}\,dx\,dy\,, \quad \phi(t) = |t|\,(\log\frac{8}{|t|})^{1-a}$$

and the following potential theoretic lemma:

LEMMA 6. *If σ is an interval of length d on $(-\pi,\pi)$, denote by $T\sigma$ an interval of length $3d$ and the same midpoint as σ. We assume that $\{\sigma_\nu\}$ are disjoint and denote by $E = \cup\,\sigma_\nu$ and $E' = \cup\,T\sigma$. There is a constant Q only depending on K such that*

$$C_K(E') \leq Q\,C_K(E)$$

provided $K(x) = O(K(2x)),\ x \to 0$.

In an outline, the proof of Theorem 2 proceeds as follows. Let $\sigma_{\nu n}$ denote the 2^n disjoint intervals of length $2\pi \cdot 2^{-n}$ on $(-\pi, \pi)$. Let λ be given and denote by $M_\alpha(f)$ the mean value of f over the interval α. We choose intervals $\sigma_1, \sigma_2, \ldots,$ such that

$$M_{\sigma_\nu}(f) \geq \lambda \tag{10.2}$$

by first choosing those $\sigma_{\nu 1}$ that satisfy (10.2), then $\sigma_{\mu 2}$ disjoint from those chosen before etc. It follows easily from the lemma that it is sufficient to prove $C\{\cup \sigma_\nu\} \leq \text{Const.}\ \|f\|^2 \cdot \lambda^{-2}$.

Let τ_ν be intervals such that $T\tau_\nu = \sigma_\nu$. We want to construct $f_1(x)$ such that $\|f_1\| \leq \text{Const.}\ \|f\|$ and $f_1(x) \equiv M_{\sigma_\nu}(f),\ x \in \tau_\nu$. We first modify f on each σ_ν according to the following rule where we have normalized σ_ν to $(-1, 1)$:

$$f_2(x) = \begin{cases} f(2x), & -\frac{1}{2} < x < \frac{1}{2} \\ f(-x - \frac{3}{2}), & -\frac{3}{4} < x < -\frac{1}{2} \\ f(x), & -1 < x < -\frac{3}{4} \\ \text{analogously on } (\frac{1}{2}, 1). & \end{cases}$$

Outside $\cup \sigma_\nu$ we define $f_2(x) = f(x)$. From (10.1) it follows that $\|f_2\|_K \leq \text{Const.}\ \|f\|_K$.

Let 4δ be the length of the shortest of the intervals σ_ν. We have the following picture:

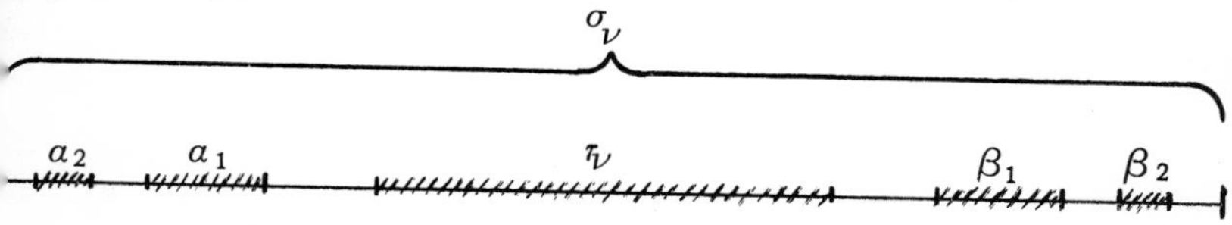

where we construct α_i and β_i until their length $< \delta$. We define

$$f_1(x) = \begin{cases} M_{\tau_\nu}(f_2) = M_{\sigma_\nu}(f), & x \in \tau_\nu; \\ M_{\alpha_i}(f_2), & x \in \alpha_i; \\ M_{\beta_i}(f_2), & x \in \beta_i; \\ \text{linear between the intervals.} \end{cases}$$

We do the same construction on each σ_ν and each complementary interval. A computation in (10.1) shows that $\|f_1\| <$ Const. $\|f_2\|$.

To complete the proof, let μ be a distribution of unit mass on $E'' = \cup \tau_\nu$. Then

$$\lambda \le \int_{E''} f_2(x)\, d\mu(x) \le \|f_2\|_K \cdot I_K(\mu)^{\frac{1}{2}} \le \text{Const. } \|f\|_K \cdot I_K(\mu)^{\frac{1}{2}}.$$

The lemma now yields Theorem 7.

§ VI. *EXISTENCE OF CERTAIN HOLOMORPHIC FUNCTIONS*

1. Let D be a connected domain in the complex z-plane, containing the point at ∞. We consider the space $H^q(D)$, $1 \leq q \leq \infty$, of holomorphic functions f in D satisfying

$$(1.1) \qquad \|f\|_q = \left\{ \iint_D |f(z)|^q dx\, dy \right\}^{\frac{1}{q}} < \infty, \quad \|f\|_\infty = \sup_{z \in D} |f(z)| .$$

The compact complement of D is denoted E. Our problem in this section is to find metrical conditions on E which guarantee that $H^q(D)$ contains non-trivial functions f. We observe that the case $q < 2$ is trivial since $(z - z_0)^{-1} - (z - z_1)^{-1}$, $z_i \in E$, always belongs to $H^q(D)$, $q < 2$. The following theorem will be proved.

THEOREM 1.

(a) $H^2(D)$ *contains non-trivial functions if and only if* $C_0(E) > 0$.

(b) $H^q(D)$ *contains non-trivial functions if* $C_{2-p}(E) > 0$, where $p^{-1} + q^{-1} = 1$, $2 < q \leq \infty$.

(c) $H^q(D)$ *contains only* $f \equiv 0$ *if* $\Lambda_{2-p}(E) < \infty$, $q < \infty$, $\Lambda_1(E) = 0$, $q = \infty$.

Proof.

(a) 1) We first assume $C_0(E) > 0$. E has non-intersecting closed subsets E_ν such that $C_0(E_\nu) > 0$, $\nu = 1, 2$. Let μ_ν be distributions of unit mass on E_ν with bounded logarithmic potentials and form $\mu = \mu_1 - \mu_2$ and

$$f(z) = \int_E \frac{d\mu(\zeta)}{\zeta - z} = \frac{a}{z^2} + \ldots, \quad |z| > R.$$

Clearly

$$\iint_{|z| > R} |f(z)|^2 dx\, dy < \infty, \quad R \text{ large enough},$$

while

$$\iint_{|z| \leq R} |f(z)|^2 dx\, dy \leq \int_E \int_E |d\mu(\zeta)|\, |d\mu(\zeta')| \iint_{|z| \leq R} \frac{dx\, dy}{|z - \zeta'|\, |z - \zeta|} \leq$$

$$\leq \text{Const.} \int_E \int_E \log \left| \frac{3R}{\zeta - \zeta'} \right| |d\mu(\zeta)|\, |d\mu(\zeta')| < \infty.$$

To see that $f(z) \not\equiv 0$ choose a system γ of analytic curves enclosing E_1. Then

$$\frac{1}{2\pi i} \int_\gamma f(z)\, dz = -\mu_1(E_1) = -1.$$

2) Assume $C_0(E) = 0$ and choose $D_1 \subset D_2 \subset \ldots \to D$, where D_ν is bounded by a finite number of analytic curves. Let g_ν be the Green's function of D_ν with pole at ∞ and let h_ν be its conjugate function. It is well known (see also next chapter) that $C_0(E) = 0$ is equivalent to $g_\nu(z) \to \infty$, $z \in D$, uniformly on inside domains. Hence if we introduce the coordinates $\zeta = \xi + i\eta = g_\nu + ih_\nu$ in D_ν and consider the domain $\Omega_\nu = \{z | 0 < g_\nu < 1\}$ we have for $f \in H^2(D)$,

$$\iint_{\Omega_\nu} |f(z)|^2 dx\, dy = \int_0^1 d\xi \int_0^{2\pi} \frac{|f|^2 d\eta}{(\frac{\partial g_\nu}{\partial n})^2} = \varepsilon_\nu \to 0, \quad \nu \to \infty.$$

On the other hand, the following estimate holds:

$$\int_0^1 d\xi \Big(\int_{g_\nu = \xi} |f(z)|\,|dz| \Big)^2 \le \int_0^1 d\xi \left\{ \int_{g_\nu = \xi} \frac{\partial g_\nu}{\partial n} |dz| \cdot \int_{g_\nu = \xi} \frac{|f|^2}{\frac{\partial g_\nu}{\partial n}} |dz| \right\} =$$

$$= 2\pi \int_0^1 \int_0^{2\pi} \frac{|f|^2}{\left(\frac{\partial g_\nu}{\partial n}\right)^2} d\eta\, d\xi = 2\pi\, \varepsilon_\nu .$$

Hence ξ_ν, $0 < \xi_\nu < 1$, exists so that

$$\int_{g_\nu = \xi_\nu} |f(z)|\,|dz| \le \sqrt{2\pi\, \varepsilon_\nu} .$$

The curves $g_\nu = \xi_\nu$ approach E uniformly as $\nu \to \infty$. Let z_0 be fixed in D. Then for $\nu > \nu_0$ since $f(\infty) = 0$

$$|f(z_0)| = \Big| \frac{1}{2\pi i} \int_{g_\nu = \xi_\nu} \frac{f(z)dz}{z - z_0} \Big| \le \text{Const.} \cdot \sqrt{2\pi\, \varepsilon_\nu} \to 0 .$$

This implies $f(z) \equiv 0$ and concludes the proof of (a).

(b) Assume $C_{2-p}(E) > 0$ and choose $\mu > 0$ with support on E so that

$$\int_E \frac{d\mu(\zeta)}{|z - \zeta|^{2-p}} \le M . \tag{1.2}$$

We shall prove that

$$f(z) = \int_E \frac{d\mu(\zeta)}{z - \zeta} = \frac{\mu(E)}{z} + \dots \qquad (\not\equiv 0)$$

belongs to $H^q(D)$. We assume $q < \infty$, $q = \infty$ being trivial.

Let $t(z)$ be a step function (= constant on each rectangle in a net) such that $t(z) > 0$ and

$$\iint_D t(z)^p dx\, dy = 1 . \tag{1.3}$$

$s = \sigma + it$ denotes a complex variable, $0 \leq \sigma \leq 1$, and we form

$$\phi(s) = \iint_D \int_E \frac{t(z)^{p - \frac{1}{2} ps}}{|z - \zeta|^{\frac{1}{2} ps + 2 - p}} \, d\mu(\zeta) dx\, dy .$$

By (1.2) and (1.3) we have $|\phi(it)| \leq M$. For $\sigma = 1$ we find by Schwarz's inequality

$$|\phi(1 + it)| \leq \left(\iint_D t(z)^p dx\, dy \right)^{\frac{1}{2}} \int_E \int_E d\mu(\zeta) d\mu(\zeta') \cdot \iint_{-\infty}^{\infty} \frac{dx\, dy}{|z - \zeta|^k |z - \zeta'|^k}$$

where $k = 2 - \frac{1}{2} p$. The last integral is $=$ Const. $|\zeta - \zeta'|^{p-2}$ and so

$$|\phi(1 + it)| \leq \text{Const. } M^{\frac{1}{2}} < \text{Const. } M .$$

By the maximum principle we have $\phi(2 - \frac{2}{p}) <$ Const. M which implies

$$\iint_D t(z)\, |f(z)|\, dx\, dy < \text{Const. } M .$$

Here $t(z)$ satisfying (1.3) is arbitrary so by the converse of Hölder's inequality

$$\iint |f(z)|^q dx\, dy < \infty .$$

(c) Assume first $q < \infty$ and that $\Lambda_{2-p}(E) = \Lambda < \infty$. Let $\{C_\nu\}_1^\infty$ be a covering of E with circles

$$C_\nu : \quad |z - z_\nu| < r_\nu$$

such that

$$\Sigma\, r_\nu^{2-p} \leq 2\, \Lambda , \qquad r_\nu \leq \rho . \tag{1.4}$$

t is a parameter $1 \leq t \leq 2$ and we consider the expanded circles

$$C_{\nu t} : \quad |z - z_\nu| < r_\nu t , \quad 1 \leq t \leq 2 .$$

The boundary of the unbounded component of the complement of $\bigcup_{\nu=1}^{n} C_{\nu t}$ is denoted Γ_t and consists of certain arcs $b_\nu(t)$ of the circumferences of $C_{\nu t}$. As t varies, $1 \le t \le 2$, $b_\nu(t)$ sweeps out a set Ω_ν. $\partial\Omega_\nu$ is piecewise a circle and we observe that Ω_ν and Ω_μ have no interior points in common. To see this, let z_0 be an interior point of Ω_ν and assume that $z_0 \in b_\nu(\tau)$. For $t > \tau$, z_0 is an interior point of $C_{\nu t}$ and hence $z_0 \notin \Gamma_t$, $t > \tau$, and so $z_0 \notin b_\mu(t)$.

Let $f(z) \in H^q(D)$. Then

$$f'(\infty) = \frac{1}{2\pi i} \int_{\Gamma_t} f(z)dz = \frac{1}{2\pi i} \int_1^2 dt \int_{\Gamma_t} f(z)dz =$$

$$= \frac{1}{2\pi i} \sum_{\nu=1}^{n} \int_0^1 dt \int_{b_\nu(t)} f(z)dz .$$

Taking absolute values, we find

$$|f'(\infty)| \le \frac{1}{2\pi} \sum_{\nu=1}^{n} \int_1^2 dt \int_{b_\nu(t)} |f(z)|\,|dz| \le \frac{1}{2\pi} \sum_{\nu=1}^{n} r_\nu^{-1} \iint_{\Omega_\nu} |f(z)|\,dx\,dy \le$$

$$(1.5) \qquad \le \frac{1}{2\pi} \sum_{\nu=1}^{n} r_\nu^{-1} \Big(\iint_{\Omega_\nu} |f(z)|^q dx\,dy\Big)^{\frac{1}{q}} \Big(\iint_{\Omega_\nu} dx\,dy\Big)^{\frac{1}{p}} \le$$

$$\le \frac{1}{2\pi} \sum_{\nu=1}^{n} r_\nu^{-1} a_\nu (3\pi r_\nu^2)^{\frac{1}{p}} \le \frac{(3\pi)^{\frac{1}{p}}}{2\pi} (\Sigma\, a_\nu^q)^{\frac{1}{q}} \cdot (\Sigma\, r_\nu^{2-p})^{\frac{1}{p}},$$

where $a_\nu{}^q$ denotes the double integral of $|f|^q$ over Ω_ν. Since Ω_ν are (essentially) disjoint, and since $\{\Omega_\nu\}$ cover a small neighbourhood D_ρ of E, we have

$$\Sigma\, a_\nu^q = \iint_{D_\rho} |f(z)|^q dx\,dy = \varepsilon(\rho) \to 0, \quad \rho \to 0 .$$

(1.5) and (1.4) then yield

$$|f'(\infty)| \leq \text{Const.}\ (2\Lambda)^{\frac{1}{p}} \epsilon(\rho)^{\frac{1}{q}} \to 0, \qquad \rho \to 0.$$

Hence $f'(\infty) = 0$. Considering in the same way $zf(z)$, $z^2 f(z), \ldots$ we find $f \equiv 0$.

(c) $q = \infty$. We can enclose E by circles C_ν so that

$$\Sigma\, r_\nu < \varepsilon.$$

Then

$$|f'(\infty)| \leq \frac{1}{2\pi} \Sigma \int_{C_\nu} |f(z)|\ |dz| \leq \|f\|_\infty \cdot \varepsilon$$

and as above we find $f \equiv 0$.

2. The space $H^\infty(D)$ is the most important case in the above Theorem 1. The existence of a non-trivial function is related to the extremal problem of maximizing the coefficient a in the development

$$f(z) = \frac{a}{z} + \ldots$$

where $\|f\|_\infty \leq 1$. The extremal function $f_\infty(z) = \frac{a}{z} + \ldots$ is conveniently discussed as limit of the corresponding extremal function for the space $H^q(D)$, as $q \to \infty$. We shall briefly outline this procedure and some of its consequences.

Consider the extremal problem

$$\text{(2.1)} \qquad \inf \|f\|_q = m_q, \quad f(z) = \frac{1}{z} + \ldots,$$

where $f \in H^q(D)$ and ∂D is assumed to consist of n analytic curves. The space H^q being uniformly convex, there exists an extremal function $f = F_q$. Let $g(z) = \beta z^{-2} + \ldots$ be analytic in D and consider $F_q + tg$. Varying the parameter t we get

(2.2)
$$\iint_D |F_q|^{q-2}\,\overline{F}_q\, g\, dx\, dy = 0\,.$$

We set

$$f_q(z) = m_q^{-1}\, F_q(z) = \frac{m_q^{-1}}{z} + \ldots$$

and

$$\phi_q(z) = |F_q(z)|^{q-2}\,\overline{F}_q(z)\, m_q^{1-q}\; |f_q|^{q-2}\,\overline{f}_q\,.$$

If $D_0 \subset D$ is a bounded domain, (2.1) and Hölder's inequality yield

(2.3)
$$\|\phi_q\|_p = 1\,, \quad \overline{\lim_{q\to\infty}} \iint_{D_0} |\phi_q(z)|\, dx\, dy \le 1\,,$$

while

(2.4)
$$\iint_D \phi_q(z)\, f_q(z)\, dx\, dy = 1\,.$$

If $h = a \cdot z^{-1} + \ldots$ belongs to H^q it is easy to see, by approximations by functions analytic in $\overline{D}$, that (2.2) holds for $g = h - a m_q f_q$ which by (2.4) implies

(2.5)
$$\iint_D \phi_q(z)\, h(z)\, dx\, dy = a\, m_q\,.$$

We now let $q = q_i \to \infty$ so that $f_{q_i} \to f_\infty$ and $\phi_{q_i} dx\, dy$ tends weakly to a set function $d\mu$. f_∞ is then an extremal function for $H^\infty(D)$, $|f_\infty| \le 1$, and the definition of ϕ_q and the maximum principle show that $S_\mu \subset \partial D$. (2.3) implies

(2.6)
$$\int_{\partial D} |d\mu| \le 1\,.$$

(2.5) implies if $h(z)$ is continuous in $\overline{D}$

(2.7)
$$\int_{\partial D} h(z)\, d\mu(z) = a\, a^{-1}\,,$$

since $\lim_{q\to\infty} m_q = a^{-1}$. Choosing $h(z) = (z-\zeta)^{-1}$, $\zeta \notin \bar{D}$, (2.7) yields

$$\int_{\partial D} \frac{d\mu(z)}{z-\zeta} \equiv a^{-1}, \quad \zeta \notin \bar{D}.$$

By the famous Riesz theorem, $d\mu(z) - \phi(z)\,dz$ where $\phi(z)$ are boundary values of a function analytic in D and

$$\int_{\Gamma_\lambda} |\phi(z)|\ |dz| \leq 1, \tag{2.8}$$

where Γ_λ are the level curves $g = \lambda$ of the Green's function of D, and finally $a^{-1} = 2\pi i\ \phi(\infty)$. Since ϕ tends strongly to its boundary values, (2.7) holds for any h, $|h| \leq 1$. We also observe that if ψ is any function satisfying (2.8) we have

$$|a\,\psi(\infty)| = \left|\frac{1}{2\pi i} \int_{\Gamma_\lambda} \psi\ f_\infty\, dz\right| \leq \frac{1}{2\pi}. \tag{2.9}$$

Hence $(2\pi a)^{-1}$ *is* $\sup|\psi(\infty)|$ *for all* ψ, *satisfying (2.8).*

Since we have equality in (2.9) for $\psi = \phi$ we can conclude (a) that $|f_\infty(z)| = 1$ a.e. on ∂D and (b) that $\phi f_\infty dz \geq 0$ on ∂D. Since the boundary ∂D is analytic we deduce that (c) ϕf_∞ is analytic on ∂D and (d) that ϕf_∞ has exactly n zeros in $\bar{D}$. In order to prove that $|f_\infty(z)| \equiv 1$ on ∂D we have to prove that

$$\int_{e_\lambda} \log|f_\infty(z)|\ |dz| \to 0, \text{ if } \int_{e_\lambda} |dz| \to 0,\ \lambda \to 0,\ e_\lambda \subset \Gamma_\lambda.$$

We have

$$\int_{e_\lambda} \log|f_\infty(z)|\ |dz| = \int_{e_\lambda} \log|f_\infty \phi|\ |dz| - \int_{e_\lambda} \log|\phi|\ |dz| \geq$$
$$\geq o(1) - \int_{e_\lambda} \overset{+}{\log}|\phi|\ |dz| \geq$$
$$\geq o(1) - \int_{e_\lambda} |\phi|^{\frac{1}{2}}\ |dz| \geq$$

$$\geq o(1) - \left(\int_{e\lambda} |dz| \right)^{\frac{1}{2}} \int_{e\lambda} |\phi|\ |dz| = o(1).$$

Hence (e) $|f_\infty(z)| \equiv 1$ *on* ∂D *and* f_∞ *is analytic on* ∂D, which then by (c) yields (f) that ϕ *is analytic on* ∂D. (e) implies that $f_\infty(z)$ has at least n zeros and so by (d) that (g) $f_\infty(z)$ *has exactly* n *zeros and* $\phi \neq 0$ *in* $\overline{D}$.

Now let D be an arbitrary domain for which $H^\infty(D)$ contains non-trivial functions. Then $f \in H^\infty$ exists with $a \neq 0$. Let D_n be approximations to D, $D_1 \subset D_2 \subset \ldots \to D$, and let $f_n(z) = a_n z^{-1} + \ldots$ be an extremal function of D_n. Clearly $a_n \geq a > 0$ and $\lim a_n = a$. We apply (2.7) to the function

$$\frac{f_n(z) - f_n(\zeta)}{z - \zeta} = -\frac{f_n(\zeta)}{z} + \ldots, \quad \zeta \in D_n,$$

and find

$$f_n(\zeta) = \int_{\partial D_n} \frac{f_n(z)\,\phi_n(z)\,dz}{z-\zeta} \cdot \left\{ \int_{\partial D_n} \frac{\phi_n(z)}{z-\zeta}\,dz - a_n^{-1} \right\}^{-1}.$$

We choose $n_i \to \infty$ so that $f_{n_i}\phi_{n_i}dz = |\phi_{n_i}|\ |dz| \to dp$, a distribution of unit mass on ∂D. $f_{n_i} \to f$, an extremal function for D and

$$f(\zeta) = \int_{\partial D} \frac{dp(z)}{z-\zeta} \{\Phi(z) - a^{-1}\}, \tag{2.10}$$

where $\Phi(\infty) = 0$. Now let $f_\infty(z) = az^{-1} + \ldots$ be an arbitrary extremal function for D and apply (2.7) for $h = f_\infty$ and the domain D_n:

$$f_\infty(z) = \int_{\partial D_n} \frac{f_\infty(z)\,\phi_n(z)dz}{z-\zeta} \cdot \left\{ \int_{\partial D_n} \frac{\phi_n(z)}{z-\zeta}\,dz - a_n^{-1} \right\}^{-1}.$$

Since $|f_\infty \phi_n dz| \leq |\phi_n|\ |dz|$, while on the other hand

$$\int_{\partial D_{n_i}} f_\infty \phi_{n_i} dz \to 1,$$

it follows that

$$f_\infty \phi_{n_i} dz \to dp .$$

We thus obtain the same representation (2.10) for f_∞ as for f. Hence *the extremal* $f_\infty(z)$ *is unique even in the most general case.*

3. We shall finally discuss the existence of analytic functions with finite Dirichlet integral outside a set E situated on a smooth curve Γ and shall prove the following theorem. To avoid the complications depending on the change of sign of $\log \frac{1}{r}$, we use the classical $C_0'(E) = \exp\{C_0(E)^{-1}\}$ with obvious definition if E is large.

THEOREM 2. *Let* E *be a closed subset of a simple closed curve* Γ *with continuously varying curvature. Outside* E *there exists a non-trivial analytic function* $f(z)$ *with finite Dirichlet integral if and only if* $C_0'(\Gamma - E) < C_0'(\Gamma)$. *This inequality is thus independent of the choice of* Γ.

Proof.

1) We first assume that Γ is the unit circle ω.

a) Assume $C_0'(\omega - E) < C_0'(\omega) = 1$.

We choose finite sums of intervals $F_n \nearrow \omega - E$ and let $u_n(z)$ be the equilibrium potentials of F_n of distributions μ_n of unit masses on F_n, $u_n \equiv \gamma_n$ on F_n. We form

$$f_n(z) = \frac{1}{2\pi}\int_{-\pi}^{\pi} \frac{e^{i\phi}+z}{e^{i\phi}-z}\,(u_n(e^{i\phi}) - \gamma_n)d\phi = \frac{1}{2\pi}\int_{\omega - F_n} .$$

$f_n(z)$ is holomorphic outside $\omega - F_n$, $f_n(0) = -\gamma_n$ and $f_n(\infty) = \gamma_n$. We develop $f_n(z)$ in series:

$$f_n(z) = \begin{cases} -\gamma_n + 2 \sum\limits_{\nu=1}^{\infty} z^\nu \dfrac{1}{2\pi} \displaystyle\int_{-\pi}^{\pi} u_n(e^{i\phi})\, e^{-i\nu\phi} d\phi = \sum\limits_0^\infty a_\nu z^\nu, & |z| < 1, \\[2ex] \gamma_n - 2 \sum\limits_{\nu=1}^{\infty} z^{-\nu} \dfrac{1}{2\pi} \displaystyle\int_{-\pi}^{\pi} u_n(e^{i\phi})\, e^{i\nu\phi} d\phi = \sum\limits_0^\infty b_\nu z^{-\nu}, & |z| > 1. \end{cases}$$

Observing that

$$a_\nu = \frac{1}{\nu} \int_{-\pi}^{\pi} e^{-i\nu\phi}\, \mu_n(\phi),$$

we find

$$\iint\limits_{|z|<1} |f_n'(z)|^2\, dx\, dy = \pi \sum_1^\infty \nu\, |a_\nu|^2 = \pi\, I(\mu_n) < M'.$$

The integral over $|z| > 1$ is estimated in the same way and hence

$$\iint |f_n'(z)|^2\, dx\, dy < M.$$

The function $f(z) = \lim f_{n_\nu}(z)$ is thus non-trivial, since $\lim \gamma_n > 0$, and has finite Dirichlet integral.

b) We now assume that $C_0(\omega - E) = 1$ and construct F_n and μ_n as above. Since, if $d\mu_{n_\nu} \to d\mu$, $u_\mu \leq 0$ and the equilibrium distribution for ω is unique we must have

$$d\mu_n \to \frac{1}{2\pi}\, d\theta, \quad n \to \infty,$$

whence

$$\mu_\nu^{(n)} = \int_{-\pi}^{\pi} e^{i\nu\phi}\, d\mu_n(\phi)$$

have the properties

$$\mu_0^{(n)} = 1$$

and

$$\sum_{\nu \neq 0} \frac{1}{|\nu|} |\mu_\nu^{(n)}|^2 \to 0, \quad n \to \infty.$$

If $f(z)$ satisfies the conditions of the theorem, then

$$u(z) = \mathrm{Re}\,\{f(z) - \overline{f(\overline{z}^{-1})}\} = \sum_{-\infty}^{\infty} c_\nu r^{|\nu|} e^{i\nu\theta}, \quad r < 1,$$

is harmonic outside E and $\Sigma\, |\nu|\, |c_\nu|^2 < \infty$. On F_n, $u(e^{i\theta}) = 0$ whence

$$0 = \lim_{r \to 1} \int_{F_n} u(re^{i\theta})\, e^{im\theta}\, d\mu_n(\theta) = \sum_\nu c_{\nu - m}\, d\mu_\nu^{(n)} =$$

$$= c_{-m} + \sum_{\nu \neq 0} c_{\nu - m}\, \mu_\nu^{(n)}.$$

This yields

$$|c_{-m}|^2 \leq \sum_{\nu \neq 0} |\nu|\, |c_{\nu - m}|^2 \cdot \sum_{\nu \neq 0} \frac{1}{|\nu|} |\mu_\nu^{(n)}|^2 \to 0, \quad n \to \infty.$$

Hence $u(z) \equiv 0$ and if $(z) \equiv \overline{f(\overline{z}^{-1})} + ic_2$. In the same way $Im\{f(z) + f(\overline{z}^{-1})\}$ is shown to be $\equiv 0$ and we find $f \equiv$ constant.

2) To be able to prove Theorem 3 for a general Γ we need a reformulation of the condition $C_0'(\Gamma - E) = C_0'(\Gamma)$. The new condition shows more clearly which properties of E that are essential. The result is formulated in the following lemma.

LEMMA 1. *Let Γ be a curve as stated in Theorem 3. Then $C_0'(\Gamma - E) = C_0'(\Gamma)$ is equivalent to the following condition. There exist mass distributions λ_n on $\Gamma - E$ so that*

(3.1) $\lambda_n \to$ *arc length* s *(weakly)*

and

(3.2) $u\lambda_n(z)$ *converge uniformly to* u_s *on* Γ.

Proof. Assume first $C_0'(\Gamma - E) = C_0'(\Gamma)$. The equilibrium distribution μ of Γ is

$$d\mu = \frac{1}{2\pi} \frac{\partial g}{\partial n} ds ,$$

where g is the Green's function. For Γ, $\frac{\partial g}{\partial n}$ is bounded from above and below. Now let μ_n be equilibrium distributions of subsets of $\Gamma - E$ so that $u_{\mu_n} \leq \gamma + \varepsilon_n$, $\varepsilon_n \to 0$. Since $\mu_n \to \mu$, the above formula for μ and $u_\mu \equiv \gamma$ on Γ show that

$$\int_{|z-\zeta|>\delta} \log \frac{1}{|z-\zeta|} d\mu_n(\zeta) > \gamma - \varepsilon ,$$

uniformly for $z \in \Gamma$ if $\delta < \delta(\varepsilon)$ and $n \geq n(\varepsilon)$. Hence

$$\int_{|z-\zeta|\leq\delta} \log \frac{1}{|z-\zeta|} d\mu_n(\zeta) < 2\varepsilon , \quad n \geq n_1(\varepsilon). \tag{3.3}$$

Then $d\lambda_n = 2\pi (\frac{\partial g}{\partial n})^{-1} d\mu_n$ also have the property (3.3), which proves one part of the lemma.

Assume now that (3.1) and (3.2) hold. Then $d\mu_n = \frac{1}{2\pi} (\frac{\partial g}{\partial n}) d\lambda_n$ also generate uniformly convergent potentials from which immediately follows that $C_0'(\Gamma - E) = C_0'(\Gamma)$.

Remark. It is clear from the proof that the lemma holds for all s for which $\frac{d\mu}{ds}$ is bounded from above and from below.

We now prove Theorem 2 by showing that the properties involved are invariant under a suitable mapping of $\Gamma \leftrightarrow \omega$.

We may assume that Γ has length $= 2\pi$ and map $\Gamma \leftrightarrow \omega$ so that the arc length between corresponding points is equal. The set E corresponds to $F \subset \omega$ and the lemma shows that $C_0'(\Gamma - E) < C_0'(\Gamma)$

if and only if $C_0'(\omega - F) < C_0(\omega)$.

We shall now prove that a non-trivial function f with finite Dirichlet integral exists outside F if and only if such a function exists outside E. The proof is the same in both directions. We assume $f(z)$ given outside E and let $z = \phi(\zeta)$ be the above mapping $\omega \to \Gamma$. For a function $g(\zeta)$ with finite Dirichlet integral outside a set $F_1 \subset \omega$, boundary values $g_1(e^{i\theta})$ and $g_2(e^{i\theta})$ from the inside and the outside exist. These functions belong to all Lebesgue classes $L^q(\omega)$ and can be used in the Cauchy formula. The same result holds for Γ as is shown by a conformal mapping. Hence $f(z)$ can be written (assuming $f(\infty) = 0$)

$$f(z) = \int_E \frac{F(z_1)}{z_1 - z}\, dz_1 = \int_\Gamma \frac{F(z_1)}{z_1 - z}\, dz_1 \; (F \equiv 0,\ z_1 \notin E), \tag{3.4}$$

where $F(z_1) \in L^q(|dz_1|)$, all $q < \infty$. We construct

$$g(\zeta) = \int_\omega \frac{F(\phi(\zeta_1))\, d\zeta_1}{\zeta_1 - \zeta}. \tag{3.5}$$

It is clear that $g(\zeta)$ is holomorphic outside F and that $g(\zeta) \not\equiv 0$ (since the set function $F(\phi)\, d\zeta_1 \not\equiv 0$; cf. the proof of Theorem 1 (a)). If we can prove that g has finite Dirichlet integral, Theorem 2 is proved.

We extend the mapping $z = \phi(\zeta)$ to e.g. the inside of ω by associating to a point ζ_0 on a certain normal to ω a point inside Γ on the corresponding normal to Γ at the same distance to Γ. Our assumption on Γ implies that the extended mapping is $1-1$ in a neighbourhood of ω and that the area elements have a quotient bounded from above and from below. Let $\zeta_0 = -i + i\delta$ and $z_0 = i\delta$ be corresponding points and let the normals meet ω resp. Γ in $-i$ resp. 0. We shall compare $g'(\zeta_0)$ and $f'(z_0)$.

In the formula (3.4) we replace z_1 by x_1 and dz_1 by dx_1 and obtain a function $f_1(z)$. We find

$$|f'(z_0) - f_1'(z_0)| \leq \int_\Gamma \frac{|F(z_1)|\,|dy_1|}{|z_0 - z_1|^2} + \int_\Gamma |F(z_1)| \left|\frac{1}{(z_0 - z_1)^2} - \frac{1}{(z_0 - x_1)^2}\right| dx_1$$

$$\leq C \int_\Gamma \frac{|F(z_1)|\,|x_1|\,|dx_1|}{\delta^2 + x_1^2} + C \int_\Gamma |F(z_1)| \frac{\delta x_1^2 + |x_1|^3}{(\delta^2 + x_1^2)^2} |dx_1| \tag{3.6}$$

$$= O(\delta^{-a}), \text{ all } a > 0,$$

since $F \in L^q(|dz_1|)$. A corresponding inequality holds for $g_1(\zeta_0)$ where in (3.5) ζ_1 and $d\zeta_1$ are replaced by ξ_1 and $d\xi_1$, $\zeta_1 = \xi_1 + i\eta_1$. We finally have the inequality

$$|f_1'(z_0) - g_1'(\zeta_0)| \leq C \cdot \int |F(z_1)|\,|(x_1 - i\delta)^{-2} - (x_1 + O(x_1^2) - i\delta)^{-2}|\,|dx_1|$$

$$= O(\delta^{-a}), \quad a > 0. \tag{3.7}$$

(3.6) and (3.7) and the remarks made above now show that $g(\zeta)$ has finite Dirichlet integral. Theorem 2 is thus proved.

§ VII. *REMOVABLE SINGULARITIES FOR HARMONIC FUNCTIONS*

1. The problem to be discussed in this chapter can quite generally be formulated as follows. Let D be a bounded region in d-dimensional space. Since the case $d = 2$ is particularly well-known and since certain modifications are necessary for this case, we assume here that $d \geq 3$. D is assumed to be bounded by a smooth outer surface Γ and a closed set E situated strictly inside Γ. H is a class of functions harmonic in D. The problem is to give metrical conditions on E which guarantee that every function in H can be extended to a harmonic function also on E. If this is possible we say that E is removable for the class H.

THEOREM 1. *A set E is removable for the following classes H if and only if E has vanishing capacity for $K(r) = r^{2-d}$:*

H_1: *The class of bounded harmonic functions;*

H_2: *The class of uniformly continuous harmonic functions;*

H_3: *The class of harmonic functions with finite Dirichlet integral.*

Proof.

1) We first assume that E has positive capacity. Then there is a distribution of unit mass on E such that

$$u(x) = \int_E \frac{d\mu(y)}{|x-y|^{d-2}} \tag{1.1}$$

is bounded and even (considering if necessary a suitable restriction of μ) uniformly continuous. Since $u(x)$ is non-constant, it is an example for H_1 and H_2. To see that $u(x)$ also belongs to H_3 we observe that

$$|\text{grad } u| \leq C_1 \int_E \frac{d\mu(y)}{|x-y|^{d-1}}$$

and hence

$$\int_D |\text{grad } u|^2 dx \leq C_1^2 \int_E \int_E d\mu(y)\, d\mu(z) \int_{-\infty}^{\infty} \frac{dx}{|x-y|^{d-1}\,|x-z|^{d-1}} =$$

$$= C_2 \int_E \int_E \frac{d\mu(y)\, d\mu(z)}{|x-z|^{d-2}} < \infty .$$

2) Assume that E has vanishing capacity and construct $E_1 \supset E_2 \supset \ldots \to E$, where E_n consists of a finite number of smooth surfaces. The corresponding domains bounded by Γ and E_n are denoted D_n.

Let $u(x)$ belong to H_1 and construct $u_1(x)$ harmonic inside a suitable surface Γ_1 inside Γ such that $u_1(x) = u(x)$ on Γ_1. We consider $v(x) = u(x) - u_1(x)$ and shall prove that $v(x) \equiv 0$ inside Γ_1, which will be denoted D'.

We form the equilibrium potential of E_n

$$p_n(x) = \int_{E_n} \frac{d\mu_n(y)}{|x-y|^{d-2}} \quad (= V_n \text{ on } E_n)$$

where by assumption $V_n \to \infty$. By the maximum principle, there is a constant C independent of n so that

$$v(x) \leq C\, V_n^{-1}\, p_n(x)$$

and since $V_n^{-1}\, p_n(x) \to 0$ in D', $v(x) \leq 0$. In the same manner we prove $v(x) \geq 0$ and so $v(x) \equiv 0$.

If $u(x)$ belongs to H_3 we construct $v(x)$ and $p_i(x)$ as above. Let $\psi(t)$ be a twice continuously differentiable function defined for all real numbers t satisfying the condition

$$\psi''(t) \equiv 0, \quad |t| \text{ large.} \tag{1.2}$$

We observe that $\Delta\psi(v(x)) = \psi''(v)\,|\text{grad } v|^2$. By Green's formula we find, if $d\sigma$ denotes the surface element and n the outer normal,

$$\int_{\partial D_i} \psi(v)\,\frac{\partial p_i}{\partial n}\,d\sigma = -\int_{D_i}(p_i - V_i)\psi''(v)|\text{grad } v|^2 dx + \psi'(0)\int_{\Gamma_1}(p_i - V_i)\frac{\partial v}{\partial n}\,d\sigma$$
$$= \int_{D_i} \psi'(v)\,(\text{grad } p_i,\ \text{grad } v)\,dx .$$

We divide the last two expressions in the above equality by V_i and let $i \to \infty$. Since

$$\int_{D_i} |\text{grad } p_i|^2 dx = O(V_i), \quad i \to \infty,$$

which is proved as in part 1) above and since $|\psi'|$ is bounded, it follows from Schwarz's inequality that the second expression tends to zero. Since also

$$\psi'(0)\int_{\Gamma_1}(p_i V_i^{-1} - 1)\,\frac{\partial v}{\partial n}\,d\sigma \to -\psi'(0)\int_{\Gamma_1}\frac{\partial v}{\partial n}\,d\sigma = -C\,\psi'(0)$$

we have

$$\int_{D'} \psi''(v)\,|\text{grad } v|^2 dx = \int_{-\infty}^{\infty} \psi''(t)\,d\mu(t) = C\,\psi'(0) \tag{1.3}$$

for all functions ψ satisfying (1.2) if $\mu(a) = \iint_{v<a} |\text{grad } v|^2 dx$. (1.3) implies $\mu(a) = C_1 a$, $a > 0$, $= C_2 a$, $a < 0$. Unless $C_1 = C_2 = 0$ this contradicts $v \in H_3$. Hence $v \equiv \text{Constant} = 0$.

2. Theorem 1 shows that if the set E has dimension $> d-2$ (i.e.

$\Lambda_\alpha(E) > 0$ for some $\alpha > d-2$) there is a uniformly continuous function u with singularities on E. On the other hand we can construct very regular harmonic functions outside a smooth surface, i.e. a set of dimension $d-1$. A result connecting these two facts is given in the following theorem.

THEOREM 2. *A set E is removable for the class H_α of harmonic functions satisfying a Lipschitz condition of order α, $0 < \alpha < 1$,*

$$|u(x) - u(x')| \leq \text{Const. } |x - x'|^\alpha, \quad x, x' \in D, \tag{2.1}$$

if and only if $\Lambda_{d-2+\alpha}(E) = 0$.

Proof.

1) We first assume that $\Lambda_{d-2+\alpha}(E) > 0$. By Theorem II.1, there is a distribution μ of unit mass on E such that

$$\mu(S) \leq C\, r^{d-2+\alpha}$$

for all spheres of radius r. We shall prove that

$$u(x) = \int_E \frac{d\mu(y)}{|x-y|^{d-2}}$$

satisfies (2.1). We define $\mu(r, x) = \mu(\{y \mid |y-x| < r\})$ and find for x, $x' \in D$, $|x - x'| = \delta$,

$$u(x) - u(x') = \int_0^\infty r^{2-d}\, d\mu(r, x) - \int_0^\infty r^{2-d}\, d\mu(r, x') =$$

$$= (d-2)\int_0^\infty (\mu(r, x) - \mu(r, x'))r^{1-d}\, dr$$

$$\leq C_1 \int_0^{2\delta} r^{d-2+\alpha} r^{1-d}\, dr + (d-2)\int_{2\delta}^\infty (\mu(r, x) - \mu(r-\delta, x))\, r^{1-d} dr$$

$$< C_2\, \delta^\alpha + (d-2)\int_\delta^\infty \mu(r, x)\, (r^{1-d} - (r+\delta)^{1-d})\, dr$$

$$< C_2\,\delta^{\alpha} + C_3 \int_{\delta}^{\infty} \frac{r^{d-2+\alpha}\delta}{r^d}\,dr = C_4\,\delta^{\alpha}.$$

Since x and x' can be interchanged we have proved (2.1).

2) We now assume that $\Lambda_{d-2+\alpha}(E) = 0$ and that $u(x)$ satisfies (2.1). We construct $v(x)$ as above and shall prove $v(x) \equiv 0$.

We can cover E by n closed spheres S_ν,

$$S_\nu : \quad |x - x_\nu| \le r_\nu$$

such that

$$\Sigma\, r_\nu^{d-2+\alpha} \le \varepsilon.$$

We assume that ε has its smallest value when the number of spheres is $\le n$. In the proof we shall also use the expanded spheres

$$S_\nu(t): \quad |x - x_\nu| \le r_\nu t, \qquad 1 \le t \le 3.$$

For $t > 1$ every point of E is strictly inside $\cup S_\nu(t) = \Sigma(t)$. The part of the boundary $\partial\Sigma(t)$ of $\Sigma(t)$ which is boundary of the unbounded component of the complement of $\Sigma(t)$ is denoted $\sigma(t) = \cup\,\sigma_\nu(t)$, where $\sigma_\nu(t)$ is $\sigma(t) \cap \partial S_\nu(t)$. Clearly $\sigma(t)$ does not meet E.

By Green's formula, we have, if the function ψ is defined by the first sign of equality below, $t > 1$,

$$(2.2) \qquad \psi(t) = \int_{D'\Sigma(t)} |\mathrm{grad}\; v|^2\, dx = \int_{\sigma(t)} v\,\frac{\partial v}{\partial n}\, d\sigma = \frac{1}{2}\int_{\sigma(t)} \frac{\partial v^2}{\partial n}\, d\sigma .$$

If $v \not\equiv$ constant, $\psi(t)$ is bounded from below in $1 < t \le 3$, if ε is small enough. We rewrite (2.2) introducing the unit sphere U. Points on U are denoted ξ and its area element dA_ξ. The part of U for which $x_\nu + t r_\nu \xi \in \sigma_\nu(t)$ is called $a_\nu(t)$. Integrating (2.2) and using these notations we find

$$(2.3)\quad -2\int_2^3 \psi(t)\,t^{1-d}\,dt = \sum_{\nu=1}^{n} r_\nu^{d-2}\int_2^3 dt \int_{a_\nu(t)} \frac{\partial}{\partial t} v^2(x_\nu + r_\nu t\xi)\,dA_\xi\,.$$

In each term to the right of (2.3) we shall now interchange the order of integration. We must then study for ξ fixed for which values of t a certain ray $x_\nu + r_\nu t\xi$ belongs to $\sigma_\nu(t)$. We distinguish four cases, the first two of which are trivial.

(a). $x_\nu + r_\nu t\xi \notin \sigma_\nu(t)$, $2 \le t \le 3$. For such a ξ we get 0 as contribution to (2.3).

(b). $x_\nu + r_\nu t\xi \in \sigma_\nu(t)$, $2 \le t \le 3$. We can evaluate the t-integration and get the contribution

$$v^2(x_\nu + 3r_\nu\xi) - v^2(x_\nu + 2r_\nu\xi) = O(r_\nu^{\alpha}).$$

(c). The remaining possibility is:

$x_\nu + r_\nu t\xi \in \sigma_\nu(t)$, $\tau_i \le t \le \tau_i'$, $i = 0, 1, 2, \dots, m$, $2 \le \tau_0 < \tau_0' < \tau_1 < \dots < \tau_m' \le 3$. For every τ_i', $i < m$, there is an index $\mu \ne \nu$ so that $x_\nu + r_\nu \tau_i'\xi \in \sigma_\mu(\tau_i')$. We here have two essentially different cases.

(c 1). $r_\mu \ge r_\nu$. If we consider the two-dimensional plane containing x_ν, x_μ and $x = x_\nu + r_\nu\tau_i'\xi$, we see that $x' = x_\nu + r_\nu t\xi$, $t > \tau_i'$, must be interior to $S_\mu(t)$ and hence $x_\nu + r_\nu t\xi \notin \sigma_\nu(t)$, $t > \tau_i'$. (c 1) can thus occur only if $i = m$.

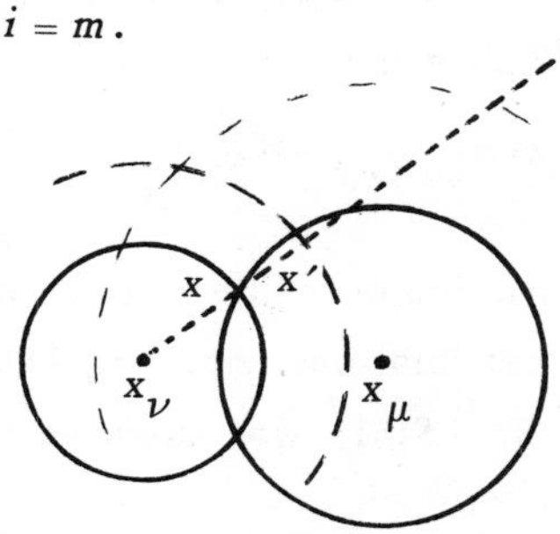

(c 2) We may thus assume $r_\mu \le r_\nu$. We first observe that $x_\nu + r_\nu t\xi$, $2 \le t \le 3$, belongs to a certain sphere $S_\mu(t)$ in a t-interval and that its length is $\le 6\, r_\mu r_\nu^{-1}$. We now consider an interval (τ_i', τ_{i+1}). The corresponding spheres $S_\mu(t)$ are $\mu = \mu_1, \ldots, \mu_k$. We can write if $\phi(t) = v^2(x_\nu + r_\nu t\xi)$,

$$\phi(\tau_{i+1}) - \phi(\tau_i') = \sum_{j=1}^{k} (\phi(s_{j+1}) - \phi(s_j)) \tag{2.4}$$

where each pair s_j, s_{j+1} belongs to one $S_{\mu_\ell}(3)$. Hence

$$|\phi(\tau_{i+1}) - \phi(\tau_i')| \le \Sigma \cdot C \cdot r_\nu^{\alpha} |s_{j+1} - s_j|^{\alpha} \le C \cdot 6^{\alpha} \sum_{j=1}^{k} r_{\mu_j}^{\alpha}. \tag{2.5}$$

We now evaluate the t-integral of the ν:th term in (2.3) and find

$$\sum_0^m (\phi(\tau_i') - \phi(\tau_i)).$$

If we add the relations (2.4) for $i = 0, 1, \ldots, m-1$, and use (2.5) we get the estimate

$$O(r_\nu^{\alpha}) + O(\Sigma^1 r_\mu^{\alpha}), \tag{2.6}$$

where Σ^1 indicates that the summation is extended over those μ such that $x_\nu + r_\nu t\xi$, $t \le 3$, meets $S_\mu(3)$.

We consider the estimate (2.6) for different points $\xi \in U$. The "area" of U for which $x_\nu + r_\nu t\xi \in S_\mu(3)$ for some t is $O(r_\mu^{d-1} r_\nu^{1-d})$. The total ν:th term in (2.3) is thus

$$O(r_\nu^{d-2+\alpha}) + O(r_\nu^{-1} \Sigma^2 r_\mu^{d-1+\alpha}), \tag{2.7}$$

where Σ^2 indicates summation over those μ for which $S_\mu(3) \cap S_\nu(3) \ne \phi$ and $r_\mu \le r_\nu$. The last relations imply $S_\mu(1) \subset S_\nu(7)$. Since the covering by the spheres $S_\nu = S_\nu(1)$ was assumed to be minimal we have

$$\Sigma^2 r_\mu^{d-2+\alpha} \le 7^{d-2+\alpha} r_\nu^{d-2+\alpha}.$$

If we use this and $r_\mu \le r_\nu$ in (2.7), we find that the ν:th term in

(2.3) $= O(r_\nu^{d-2+a})$ and so

$$\int_2^3 \psi(t)\, t^{1-d}\, dt \le \text{Const} \sum_1^n r_\nu^{d-2+a} \le \text{Const} \cdot \varepsilon .$$

Hence $\psi(t)$ cannot be bounded from below and so $v(x) \equiv$ constant, and then $v \equiv 0$, as was to be proved.

3. As an analogue of Theorem VI.1 we consider the spaces $H^p(D)$, $p \ge 1$, D a bounded region, of functions u harmonic in D such that

$$\int_D |u(x)|^p\, dx < \infty. \tag{3.1}$$

The problem of removable singularities for the spaces H^p is only interesting if $d \ge 3$ since for $d = 2$ $\log |x|$ belongs to H^p for all p. We shall prove the following theorem.

THEOREM 3. *Suppose that* $d \ge 3$ *and define* q *by* $p^{-1} + q^{-1} = 1$ *and assume* $d > 2q$. *Then if* $\Lambda_{d-2q}(E) < \infty$, E *is removable for the space* $H^p(D)$. *If* $\Lambda_a(E) > 0$ *for some* $a > d - 2q$, E *is not removable for* $H^p(D)$.

Remark. If we as usual let $p = \infty$ correspond to bounded functions, the above result is the best possible criterion in terms of Λ_a as shown by Theorem 1 and the results of Chapter III. —We also note that $|x|^{2-d}$ belongs to $H^p(D)$ if $p < d(d-2)^{-1}$ and $p = d(d-2)^{-1}$ corresponds to $d = 2q$.

For the proof of Theorem 3 we need the following

LEMMA. *Let* $\bigcup_{\nu=1}^{n} S_\nu = S$ *be a covering of* E *with spheres of radii* $< \varepsilon$ *and let* x_0 *be a fixed point of* D, $x_0 \in D - S$. *Let* $d\omega(x)$ *be the harmonic measure of a surface element* dS *of* S *of area* $d\sigma$

and situated on S_ν *of radius* r_ν. *Then there is a constant* C *only depending on* D, E *and* x_0, *such that as* $\varepsilon \to 0$

$$d\omega \leq C\, r_\nu^{-1}\, d\sigma. \tag{3.2}$$

Proof. By the principle of extension $d\omega \leq d\omega_1$ where $d\omega_1$ is the harmonic measure of the ring domain bounded by S_ν and a sphere Σ concentric to S_ν of radius R, where R is large enough. Furthermore, if S_ν is $|x| < r_\nu$,

$$\int_{S_\nu} d\omega_1 < \frac{r_\nu^{d-2}}{|x|^{d-2}} \tag{3.3}$$

and by Harnack's principle $d\omega_1$ and $d\omega_1'$ corresponding to different rotations of dS on S_ν satisfy inequalities

$$\frac{d\omega_1}{d\omega_1'} < \text{Const.} \tag{3.4}$$

Since finally $|x|$ is bounded from below at x_0, (3.3) and (3.4) imply (3.2).

Proof of Theorem 3.

1) We first assume $\Lambda_{d-2q}(E) < \infty$ and consider u satisfying (3.1). As in the other proofs in this section we may assume that $u = 0$ on $\partial D - E$ and shall prove $u \equiv 0$.

We consider a covering $S = \bigcup_{\nu=1}^{n} S_\nu$ such that $r_\nu \leq \varepsilon$ and

$$\Sigma\, r_\nu^{d-2q} \leq 2\Lambda . \tag{3.5}$$

We also consider the extended spheres $S_\nu(t)$: $|x - x_\nu| = r_\nu t$, $1 \leq t \leq$ ≤ 2, and as in the proof of Theorem VI.1 (c) we can write

$$u(x_0) = \sum_{\nu=1}^{n} \int_{\gamma_\nu(t)} u(x)\, d\omega_t(x), \tag{3.6}$$

where $d\omega_t$ are the harmonic measures described in the lemma for $S = \cup S_\nu(t)$. We integrate (3.6) with respect to t, $1 \le t \le 2$, and use (3.2) and find

$$|u(x_0)| \le C \sum_{\nu=1}^{n} r_\nu^{-1} \int_1^2 dt \int_{\gamma_\nu(t)} |u(x)|\, d\sigma . \tag{3.7}$$

$\gamma_\nu(t)$, $1 \le t \le 2$, covers a domain Ω_ν and these domains Ω_ν are except for the boundaries disjoint. (3.7) then yields by Hölder's inequality

$$\begin{aligned} |u(x_0)| &\le C \sum_{\nu=1}^{n} r_\nu^{-2} \int_{\Omega_\nu} |u(x)|\, dx \le \\ &\le C \sum_{\nu=1}^{n} r_\nu^{-2} \left\{ \int_{\Omega_\nu} |u(x)|^p\, dx \right\}^{\frac{1}{p}} \left\{ \int_{\Omega_\nu} dx \right\}^{\frac{1}{q}} \le \\ &\le C_1 \sum_{\nu=1}^{n} r_\nu^{d \cdot q^{-1} - 2} \int_{\Omega_\nu} |u(x)|^p\, dx^{\frac{1}{p}} \le \\ &\le C_1 \left\{ \int_{\Omega} |u(x)|^p\, dx \right\}^{\frac{1}{p}} \left\{ \sum_{\nu=1}^{n} r_\nu^{d-2q} \right\}^{\frac{1}{q}} . \end{aligned}$$

Here $\Omega = \cup \Omega_\nu$ is a neighbourhood of E. Choosing ε small the first factor is small while the second by (3.5) is bounded. Hence $u(x_0) = 0$ as asserted.

2) We now assume $\Lambda_\alpha(E) > 0$, $\alpha > d - 2q$, and choose a distribution of unit mass on E such that $\mu(S) \le Cr^\alpha$ for all spheres of radius r. We prove that

$$u(x) = \int \frac{d\mu(y)}{|x-y|^{d-2}}$$

belongs to H^p. We use the method of Theorem VI.1 and consider a step function $f(x) > 0$ such that

$$\int_D f(x)^q \, dx = 1 .$$

Define $\beta = p^{-1}\alpha + q^{-1}(d-2q)$ so that $d-2q < \beta < \alpha$ and consider

$$\phi(s) = \iint\limits_{D\,E} \frac{f(x)^{q(1-s)} d\mu(y) \, dx}{|x-y|^{\beta+(d-\alpha)s}} .$$

We see that $|\phi(it)| \leq M$ and $|\phi(1+it)| \leq M$, with M independent of $f(x)$. By the maximum principle,

$$\phi(p^{-1}) = \int_D f(x) \, u(x) \, dx \leq M ,$$

which then yields

$$\int_D |u(x)|^p \, dx \leq M^p .$$

SECTION REFERENCES

I. The theory of capacities is due to Choquet [150]. For Lemma 2, see Davies [186].

II. Theorem 1 is due to Frostman, Thesis, 1935. Theorems 2 and 3 were proved for $h(r) = r^s$ by Davies [186], resp. Besicovitch [57].

III. For the theory of potentials, see Frostman, Thesis. For general kernels, see Kunugui [482]. Theorem 7 is due to Kishi [461].

IV. Theorem 1 is due to Frostman, the extension essentially made by Kametani [432, 433]. —Theorem 2 was proved for $K(r) = (\log \frac{1}{r})^{-1}$ and $d = 2$ by Nevanlinna [661]. —Theorem 3, cf. Ohtsuka [683]. —Theorem 4 was proved by Erdös-Gillis for $h = (\log \frac{1}{r})^{-1}$ and also by Tsuji [958]. —Theorem 5 is given in Carleson [125].

V. Theorem 1 was proved for bounded u by Calderon [108]. He also gave the method to estimate G_n. —For $\lambda_n = n^{\alpha}$, Theorem 2 was proved $(\alpha = 1)$ by Beurling [69] and Salem-Zygmund [790]. For the general result, see Temko [906]. —For harmonic functions and $\alpha = 0$, Theorem 3 is given in Beurling [69], for general functions $(\alpha = 0)$ in Deny [200]. —For Theorem 4 and radial approach, see Beurling [69] and Carleson [121], for non-tangential approach and and $\alpha = 0$ Tsuji [943]. —For Theorem 5, see Carleson [121]. —For (9.5), see Carleson [127]. Section 9 appeared in Carleson, Ann. Inst. Fourier, 15 (1965) 59–64.

VI. The result of Theorem 1 for $q = 2$ is well-known. —The extremal problems of § 2 was first studied by Ahlfors [4] and Garabedian [282]. —For Theorem 3, see Ahlfors-Beurling [7].

VII. Theorem 1 is classical. —Theorem 2 was proved in Carleson [121].

NOTE: To save space, references are made only to Mathematical Reviews (*M.R.*).

[1] ACCOLA, R., On semi-parabolic Riemann surfaces. *M.R. 29*, p. 462.

[2] AGMON, S., A property of quasi-conformal mappings. *M.R. 16*, p. 686.

[3] AGNEW, R. P., On translations of functions and sets. *M.R. 1*, p. 296.

[4] AHLFORS, L., Bounded analytic functions. *M.R. 9*, p. 24.

[5] ____ Remarks on the classification of open Riemann surfaces. *M.R. 13*, p. 338.

[6] ____ On the characterization of hyperbolic Riemann surfaces. *M.R. 14*, p. 970.

[7] AHLFORS, L. and BEURLING, A., Conformal invariants and function-theoretic null-sets. *M.R. 12*, p. 171.

[8] AHLFORS, L. and HEINS, M., Questions of regularity connected with the Phragmén-Lindelöf principle. *M.R. 10*, p. 522.

[9] AHLFORS, L. and ROYDEN, H. L., A counterexample in the classification of open Riemann surfaces. *M.R. 14*, p. 864.

[10] AHLFORS, L. and SARIO, L., Riemann surfaces. *M.R. 22*, p. 961.

[11] ALEXITS, G., Sur la convergence des series de polynomes orthogonaux. *M.R. 5*, p. 262.

[12] ____ Sur la sommation forte des series orthogonales. *M.R. 7*, p. 293.

[13] ____ Sur la convergence des séries lacunaires. *M.R. 10*, p. 113.

[14] ____ Sur la convergence d'une classe de séries orthonormales. *M.R. 10*, p. 701.

[15] ____ Sur la convergence des series orthonormales lacunaires. *M.R. 10*, p. 701.

[16] ____ Sur la convergence et la sommabilité presque partout des series de polynomes orthogonaux. *M.R. 11*, p. 659.

[17] ____ Sur les sommes de fonctions orthogonales. *M.R. 14*, p. 1081.

[18] ____ The significance of the Lebesgue functions for the problem of convergence of expansions in orthogonal polynomials. *M.R. 14*, p. 1083.

[19] ____ Sur la sommabilité des series orthogonales. *M.R. 15*, p. 788.

[20] ____ Über die Konvergenz der Orthogonal-polynomentwicklungen. *M.R. 17*, p. 257.

[21] ____ Eine Bemerkung zur starken Summierbarkeit der Orthogonalreihen. *M.R. 17*, p. 843.

[22] ____ Ein Summationssatz für Orthogonalreihen. *M.R. 18*, p. 124.

[23] ____ Sur la convergence et la sommabilité des séries orthogonales lacunaires. *M.R. 20*, p. 35.

[24] ____ Über die Konvergenz fast überall der Orthogonalreihen bei jeder Anordnung ihrer Glieder. *M.R. 24A*, p. 405.

[25] ____ Konvergenzprobleme der Orthogonalreihen. *M.R. 28*, p. 1024.

[26] ALEXITS, G. und KRALIK, D., Über die absolute Summierbarkeit und die Konvergenz der Orthogonalreihen. *M.R. 27*, p. 349.

[27] ALEXITS, G. und TANDORI, K., Über das Konvergenzverhalten einer Klasse von Orthogonalreihen. *M.R. 24A*, p. 406.

[28] ANDREYAN KAZAKU, K., Quasi-conformal mappings. *M.R. 21*, p. 781.

[29] ARBAULT, J., Sur l'ensemble de convergence absolue d'une série trigonométrique. *M.R. 14*, p. 1080.

[30] ARIMA, K., On a meromorphic function in the unit circle whose Nevanlinna's characteristic function is bounded. *M.R. 12*, p. 692.

[31] ____ On harmonic measure functions in some regions. *M.R. 12*, p. 692.

[32] ____ On the zeros of integral functions of integral order. *M.R. 14*, p. 259.

[33] ARONSZAJN, N. and SMITH, K. T., Theory of Bessel potentials. *M.R. 26*, p. 285.

[34] ARSOVE, M. G., On the definition of an analytic function. *M.R. 16*, p. 683.

[35] ____ The Looman-Menchoff theorem and some subharmonic function analogues. *M.R. 16*, p. 1108.

[36] ____ The Lusin-Privalov theorem for subharmonic functions. *M.R. 28*, p. 804.

[37] BADER, R. et PARREAU, M., Domaines non compacts et classification des surfaces de Riemann. *M.R. 12*, p. 603.

[38] BAGEMIHL, F., On power series with unbounded cluster sets, and functions of class H_2 with meagre sets of radial continuity. *M.R. 19*, p. 22.

[39] ____ On the set of values assumed by holomorphic functions near essential singularities. *M.R. 19*, p. 129.

[40] ____ Some approximation theorems for normal functions. *M.R. 28*, p. 437.

[41] ____ Some boundary properties of normal functions bounded on non-tangential arcs. *M.R. 28*, p. 801.

[42] BAGEMIHL, F., PIRANIAN, G. and YOUNG, G. S., Intersections of cluster sets. *M.R. 22*, p. 1375.

[43] BAGEMIHL, F. and PIRANIAN, G., Absolutely convergent power series. *M.R. 24A*, p. 609.

[44] BAGEMIHL, F. and SEIDEL, W., Regular functions with prescribed measurable boundary values almost everywhere. *M.R. 17*, p. 249.

[45] ____ Koebe arcs and Fatou points of normal functions. *M.R. 25*, p. 1004.

[46] BARI, N. K., On primitive functions and trigonometric series converging almost everywhere. *M.R. 14*, p. 40.

[47] ____ On primitive functions and trigonometric series converging almost everywhere. *M.R. 14*, p. 867.

[48] ____ Trigonometric series. *M.R. 23A*, p. 650.

[49] BARRY, P. D., The minimum modulus of integral functions of small order. *M.R. 23A*, p. 55.

[50] ____ The minimum modulus of small integral and subharmonic functions. *M.R. 25*, p. 614.

[51] BAUER, H., Axiomatische Behandlung des Dirichletschen Problems für elliptische und parabolische Differentialgleichungen. *M.R. 26*, p. 310.

[52] BAXTER, G., An ergodic theorem with weighted averages. *M.R. 29*, p. 457.

[53] BELLMAN, R., Fourier integrals. *M.R. 4*, p. 272.

[54] ____ Random summability and Fourier series. *M.R. 5*, p. 66.

[55] ____ Lambert summability of orthogonal series. *M.R. 5*, p. 117.

[56] BERTRANDIAS, F., Sur les fonctions analytiques possédant une certaine propriété arithmétique. *M.R. 20*, p. 402.

[57] BESICOVITCH, A. S., On existence of subsets of finite measure of sets of infinite measure. *M.R. 14*, p. 28.

[58] ____ On approximations in measure to Borel sets by F_σ-sets. *M.R. 15*, p. 943.

[59] ____ On density of perfect sets. *M.R. 18*, p. 24.

[60] ____ On density of linear sets. *M.R. 19*, p. 639.

[61] ____ Tangential properties of sets and arcs of infinite linear measure. *M.R. 22*, p. 1892.

[62] _____ Metric property of linear sets. *M.R. 24A*, p. 365.

[63] _____ On one-sided densities of arcs of positive two-dimensional measure. *M.R. 29*, p. 42.

[64] BESICOVITCH, A. S. and MORAN, P. A., The measure of product on cylinder sets. *M.R. 8*, p. 18.

[65] BESICOVITCH, A. S. and SHOENBERG, I. J., On Jordan arcs and Lipschitz classes of functions defined on them. *M.R. 25*, p. 35.

[66] BESICOVITCH, A. S. and TAYLOR, S. J., On the complementary intervals of a linear closed set of zero Lebesgue measure. *M.R. 16*, p. 344.

[67] BEST, E., A closed dimensionless linear set. *M.R. 1*, p. 302.

[68] _____ A theorem on Hausdorff measure. *M.R. 2*, p. 353.

[69] BEURLING, A., Ensembles exceptionnels. *M.R. 1*, p. 226.

[70] _____ Sur les spectres des fonctions. *M.R. 11*, p. 429.

[71] BEURLING, A. and AHLFORS, L., The boundary correspondence under quasi-conformal mappings. *M.R. 19*, p. 258.

[72] BEYER, W. A., Cardinality of level sets of Rademacher series whose coefficients form a geometric progression. *M.R. 25*, p. 250.

[73] _____ Hausdorff dimension of level sets of some Rademacher series. *M.R. 25*, p. 792.

[74] BILLARD, P., Sur la presque convergence des suites. *M.R. 22*, p. 659.

[75] _____ Sur la sommabilité des séries de fonctions orthogonales. *M.R. 24A*, p. 284.

[76] _____ Condition nécessaire pour que la fonction aléatoire $f(x)$ définie par la série de Fourier aléatoire $\sum_{n=1}^{\infty} \pm a_n \cos nx$ soit presque surement bornée. *M.R. 26*, p. 1267.

[77] BILLINGSLEY, P., Hausdorff dimension in probability theory, II. *M.R. 22*, p. 1893.

[78] _____ Hausdorff dimension in probability theory. *M.R. 24A*, p. 323.

[79] BISHOP, E., A general Rudin-Carleson theorem. *M.R. 24A*, p. 614.

[80] BJÖRCK, G., Distributions of positive mass, which maximize a certain generalized energy integral. *M.R. 17*, p. 1198.

[81] BLUMENTHAL, R. M. and GETOOR, R. K., Some theorems on stable processes. *M.R. 22*, p. 1714.

[82] _____ A dimension theorem for sample functions of stable processes. *M.R. 22*, p. 2174.

[83] ____ The dimension of the set of zeros and the graph of a symmetric stable process. *M.R.* *25*, p. 313.

[84] ____ Local times for Markov processes. *M.R.* *29*, p. 554.

[85] BOAS, R. P. Jr., Poisson's summation formula in L^2. *M.R.* *8*, p. 457.

[86] ____ Asymptotic properties of functions of exponential type. *M.R.* *15*, p. 517.

[87] BOBROV, A. A., A criterium for the weak convergence of a sequence of monotone functions. *M.R.* *26*, p. 54.

[88] BOCHNER, S. and IZUMI, S., Strong law of large numbers for sequences of almost periodic functions. *M.R.* *21*, p. 1211.

[89] BOCLÉ, J., Sur la théorie ergodique. *M.R.* *25*, p. 608.

[90] BÖGEL, K., Bedingungen für die Existenz einer Punktmenge, auf der die Gleichung $f''_{xy} = f''_{yx}$ erfüllt ist. *M.R.* *29*, p. 453.

[91] BOHMAN, H., On a class of orthogonal series. *M.R.* *12*, p. 21.

[92] BONDI, I. L., Functions which are almost everywhere A-integrable. *M.R.* *25*, p. 424.

[93] BOREL, E., Sur l'addition vectorielle des ensembles de mesure nulle. *M.R.* *10*, p. 106.

[94] ____ Sur la somme vectorielle de deux ensembles de mesure nulle dont un seul est parfait. *M.R.* *10*, p. 359.

[95] BORGEN, S., Note on Poisson's formula. *M.R.* *7*, p. 248.

[96] DE BRANGES, L., A comparison theorem for spaces of entire functions. *M.R.* *26*, p. 983.

[97] BREIMAN, L., The strong law of large numbers for a class of Markov chains. *M.R.* *22*, p. 1460.

[98] BRELOT, M., Sur la mesure harmonique et le problème de Dirichlet. *M.R.* *7*, p. 522.

[99] ____ A new proof of the fundamental theorem of Kellog-Evans on the set of irregular points in the Dirichlet problem. *M.R.* *17*, p. 474.

[100] ____ Existence theorem for n-capacities. *M.R.* *18*, p. 296.

[101] ____ Nouvelle démonstration du théorème fondamental sur la convergence des potentiels. *M.R.* *18*, p. 475.

[102] ____ La convergence des fonctions surharmoniques et des potentiels généralisés. *M.R.* *21*, p. 943.

[103] _____ Eléments de la théorie classique du potentiel. *M.R. 21*, p. 945.

[104] BRELOT, M. et CHOQUET, G., Le théorème de convergence en théorie du potentiel. *M.R. 19*, p. 261.

[105] BROMAN, A., On two classes of trigonometrical series. *M.R. 9*, p. 182.

[106] BROWN, A., On the Lebesgue convergence theorem. *M.R. 25*, p. 608.

[107] BROWN, L., SHIELDS, A. and ZELLER, K., On absolutely convergent exponential sums. *M.R. 26*, p. 66.

[108] CALDERÓN, A. P., On a theorem of Marcinkiewicz and Zygmund. *M.R. 11*, p. 357.

[109] CALDERÓN, A. P. and ZYGMUND, A., Local properties of solutions of elliptic partial differential equations. *M.R. 25*, p. 66.

[110] _____ A note on local properties of solutions of elliptic differential functions. *M.R. 25*, p. 827.

[111] _____ On the differentiability of functions which are of bounded variation in Tonelli's sense. *M.R. 27*, p. 306.

[112] CALUGARÉANO, G., Sur la suite des diamètres successifs d'un ensemble plan. *M.R. 1*, p. 109.

[113] _____ Sur une représentation conforme des domaines multiplement connexes. *M.R. 7*, p. 424.

[114] CARAMAN, P., On the N-property for continuous n-dimensional mappings. *M.R. 28*, p. 435.

[115] _____ The property (N) for n-dimensional quasiconformal mappings. *M.R. 28*, p. 435.

[116] _____ Contributions à la théorie des représentations quasiconformes n-dimensionnelles. *M.R. 28*, p. 616.

[117] _____ Le jacobien et les dilatations des représentations quasiconformes à n-dimensions. *M.R. 28*, p. 616.

[118] CARGO, G. T., Angular and tangential limits of Blaschke products and their successive derivatives. *M.R. 25*, p. 45.

[119] _____ The segmental variation of Blaschke products. *M.R. 26*, p. 503.

[120] _____ Some geometric aspects of functions of Hardy class H^p. *M.R. 27*, p. 1125.

[121] CARLESON, L., On a class of meromorphic functions and its associated exceptional sets. *M.R. 11*, p. 427.

[122] ____ On null-sets for continuous analytic functions. *M.R. 13*, p. 23.

[123] ____ Sets of uniqueness for functions regular in the unit circle. *M.R. 14*, p. 261.

[124] ____ Representations of continuous functions. *M.R. 18*, p. 798.

[125] ____ On the connection between Hausdorff measures and capacity. *M.R. 19*, p. 1047.

[126] ____ A remark on Picard's theorem. *M.R. 24A*, p. 41.

[127] ____ Interpolations by bounded analytic functions and the Corona problem. *M.R. 25*, p. 1005.

[128] ____ On the existence of boundary values for harmonic functions in several variables. *M.R. 28*, p. 440.

[129] ____ Removable singularities of continuous harmonic functions in R^m *M.R. 28*, p. 1003.

[130] CARTAN, H., Capacité extérieure et suites convergentes de potentiels. *M.R. 5*, p. 146.

[131] ____ Sur les suites de potentiels de masses ponctuelles. *M.R. 5*, p. 146.

[132] ____ Théorie générale du balayage en potentiel newtonien. *M.R. 8*, p. 581.

[133] CARTWRIGHT, M. L. and COLLINGWOOD, E. F., The radial limits of functions meromorphic in a circular disc. *M.R. 24A*, p. 41.

[134] CAVRILOV, V. I., The cluster set of functions pseudo-analytic in the unit circle. *M.R. 26*, p. 282.

[135] CERETELI, O. D., On the indefinite *A*-integral and on Fourier series. *M.R. 26*, p. 495.

[136] ____ Fourier series and metric properties of functions. *M.R. 27*, p. 774.

[137] CESARI, L., Quasi-additive set functions and the concept of integral over a variety. *M.R. 26*, p. 58.

[138] CETKOVIĆ, S., Un théorème de la théorie des fonctions. *M.R. 19*, p. 946.

[139] CHACON, R. V., Operator averages. *M.R. 26*, p. 57.

[140] ____ An ergodic theorem for operators satisfying norm conditions. *M.R. 26*, p. 977.

[141] ____ Convergence of operator averages. *M.R. 28*, p. 794.

[142] ____ Linear operators in L_1. *M.R. 28*, p. 794.

[143] CHANG, H., Approximatively analytic functions of bounded type and boundary behaviour of solutions of elliptic partial differential equations. *M.R. 17*, p. 145.

[144] CHEN, K.-K., On the series of orthogonal polynomials. *M.R. 19*, p. 545.

[145] ____ The summability of the series of orthogonal polynomials. *M.R. 24A*, p. 406.

[146] ____ On the convergence and summability of trigonometrical series and series of orthogonal polynomials. *M.R. 27*, p. 775.

[147] CHEN, Y.-M., On conjugate functions. *M.R. 28*, p. 642.

[148] ____ Remark on uniqueness of summable trigonometric series associated with conjugate series. *M.R. 28*, p. 642.

[149] CHOQUET, G., Ensembles singuliers et structure des ensembles mesurables pour les mesures de Hausdorff. *M.R. 9*, p. 419.

[150] ____ Theory of capacities. *M.R. 18*, p. 295.

[151] ____ Potentiels sur un ensemble de capacité nulle. Suites de potentiels. *M.R. 19*, p. 406.

[152] ____ Capacitabilité en potentiel logarithmique. *M.R. 21*, p. 146.

[153] CHOW, H. C., On the summability factors of Fourier series. *M.R. 4*, p. 37.

[154] ____ An extension of a theorem of Zygmund and its application. *M.R. 15*, p. 788.

[155] ____ Some new criteria for the absolute summability of a Fourier series and its conjugate series. *M.R. 17*, p. 32.

[156] CHOW, Y. S., Convergence theorems of martingales. *M.R. 27*, p. 169.

[157] CHUNG, K. L., ERDÖS, P. and SIRAO, T., On the Lipschitz's condition for Brownian motion. *M.R. 22*, p. 2173.

[158] CIESIELSKI, Z. and TAYLOR, S. J., First passage times and sojourn times for Brownian motion in space and the exact Hausdorff measure of the sample path. *M.R. 26*, p. 157.

[159] CIGLER, J., Hausdorffsche Dimensionen spezieller Punktmengen. *M.R. 25*, p. 793.

[160] COLLINGWOOD, E. F., On the linear and angular cluster sets of functions meromorphic in the unit circle. *M.R. 16*, p. 460.

[161] ____ On a theorem of Eggleston concerning cluster sets. *M.R. 17*, p. 600.

[162] ____ Cluster sets of arbitrary functions. *M.R. 22*, p. 1376.

[163] COLLINGWOOD, E. F. and CARTWRIGHT, M. L., Boundary theorems for a function meromorphic in the unit circle. *M.R. 14*, p. 260.

[164] COLLINGWOOD, E. F. et LOHWATER, A., Inégalités relatives aux défauts d'une fonction méromorphe dans le cercle-unité. *M.R. 18*, p. 797.

[165] ____ Applications of the theory of cluster sets to a class of meromorphic functions. *M.R. 18*, p. 884.

[166] COLLINGWOOD, E. F. and PIRANIAN, G., Asymmetric prime ends. *M.R. 24A*, p. 614.

[167] CONSTANTINESCU, C., Sur le comportement d'une fonction analytique à la frontière idéale d'une surface de Riemann. *M.R. 22*, p. 644.

[168] ____ Über die Klassifikation der Riemannschen Flächen. *M.R. 22*, p. 2091.

[169] ____ Ideale Randkomponenten einer Riemannschen Fläche. *M.R. 23A*, p. 52.

[170] ____ Dirichletsche Abbildungen. *M.R. 26*, p. 278.

[171] CONSTANTINESCU, C. et CORNEA, A., Comportement des transformations analytiques des surfaces de Riemann sur la frontière de Martin. *M.R. 21*, p. 781.

[172] ____ Über einige Probleme von M. Heins. *M.R. 22*, p. 805.

[173] ____ Le théorème de Beurling et la frontière idéale de Kuramochi. *M.R. 25*, p. 42.

[174] ____ Analytische Abbildungen Riemannscher Flächen. *M.R. 28*, p. 44.

[175] ____ Ideale Ränder Riemannscher Flächen. *M.R. 28*, p. 615.

[176] COOPER, J. L. B., The uniqueness of trigonometrical integrals. *M.R. 6*, p. 126.

[177] COOPER, R., Transformations of enumerable sets which are dense in an interval. *M.R. 1*, p. 107.

[178] CORNEA, A., On the behaviour of analytic functions in the neighbourhood of the boundary of a Riemann surface. *M.R. 20*, p. 402.

[179] COSSAR, I., The Bohr spectrum of a function. *M.R. 27*, p. 54.

[180] COTLAR, M. and PANZONE, R., Generalized potential operators. *M.R. 24A*, p. 156.

[181] CROFT, H. T., A note on a Darboux continuous function. *M.R. 26*, p. 970.

[182] DANILJUK, I. I., On Hilbert's problem with measurable coefficients. *M.R. 23A*, p. 336.

[183] DAVIS, P. and POLLAK, H., On an equivalent definition of the transfinite diameter. *M.R. 13*, p. 842.

[184] DAVIES, R.O., A property of Hausdorff measure. *M.R. 17*, p. 595.

[185] ____ Non σ-finite closed subsets of analytic sets. *M.R. 17*, p. 954.

[186] ____ Subsets of finite measure in analytic sets. *M.R. 14*, p. 733.

[187] DAVYDOV, N. A., Generalization of some theorems on the convergence of power and trigonometric series. *M.R. 13*, p. 340.

[188] ____ On a false theorem of Daiovic. *M.R. 19*, p. 642.

[189] DELPORTE, I., Convergence uniforme presque sûre de séries de fonctions aléatoires normales presque sûrement continues. Application à l'étude de la fonction du mouvement brownien de Wiener-Lévy. *M.R. 26*, p. 1329.

[190] ____ Extension des conditions suffisantes pour la construction de fonctions aléatoires normales, presque sûrement continues, possédant une covariance donnée. *M.R. 26*, p. 1329.

[191] ____ Un critère de convergence forte presque sûre des sommes d'éléments aléatoires independants dans un espace de Banach. *M.R. 27*, p. 820.

[192] DENČEV, R., A non-linear boundary-value problem in theory of analytic functions, arising in quantum field theory. *M.R. 27*, p. 737.

[193] DENJOY, A., Sur certaines séries de Taylor admettant leur cercle de convergence comme coupure essentielle. *M.R. 1*, p. 9.

[194] ____ Sur les séries de Taylor admettant leur cercle de convergence comme coupure. *M.R. 1*, p. 306.

[195] ____ Sur la représentation conforme. *M.R. 5*, p. 115.

[196] ____ Sur la représentation conforme. *M.R. 7*, p. 287.

[197] ____ Lecons sur le calcul des coefficients d'une série trigonométrique, Tome III. *M.R. 8*, p. 260.

[198] DENY, J., Sur les infinis d'un potentiel. *M.R. 8*, p. 380.

[199] ____ Un théorème sur les ensembles effilés. *M.R. 9*, p. 509.

[200] ____ Les potentiels d'énergie finie. *M.R. 12*, p. 98.

[201] DEVINATZ, A. and HIRSCHMAN, I. I. Jr., Multiplier transformations on $\ell^{2,a}$. *M.R. 21*, p. 691.

[202] DINGHAS, A., Zur Werteverteilung einer Klasse transzendenter Funktionen. *M.R. 1*, p. 113.

[203] DOLZENKO, E. P., The removability of singularities of analytic functions. *M.R. 27*, p. 1123.

[204] DONOGHUE, W. F. Jr., Remarks on potential theory. *M.R. 26*, p. 69.

[205] ____ Functions which are polynomials on a sense set.. *M.R. 29*, p. 455.

[206] DOOB, J. L., Brownian motion on a Green space. *M.R. 21*, p. 976.

[207] ____ Probability theory and the first boundary value problem. *M.R. 21*, p. 977.

[208] ____ A relativized Fatou theorem. *M.R. 21*, p. 1082.

[209] ____ Boundary limit theorems for a half-space. *M.R. 22*, p. 144.

[210] ____ Conditional Brownian motion and the boundary limits of harmonic functions. *M.R. 22*, p. 144.

[211] ____ A Markov chain theorem. *M.R. 22*, p. 180.

[212] ____ Relative limit theorems in analysis. *M.R. 23A*, p. 622.

[213] ____ A relative limit theorem for parabolic functions. *M.R. 24A*, p. 514.

[214] ____ A ratio operator limit theorem. *M.R. 29*, p. 127.

[215] DOWIDAR, A. F. and PETERSEN, G. M., Summability of subsequences. *M.R. 26*, p. 101.

[216] DRAGILEW, M., On local convergence of basis series. *M.R. 27*, p. 939.

[217] DUFRESNOY, J., Sur les fonctions méromorphes à caractéristique bornée. *M.R. 5*, p. 116.

[218] ____ Sur les fonctions méromorphes et univalentes dans le cercle unité. *M.R. 7*, p. 56.

[219] DUGUÉ, D., Sur la convergence presque certaine des séries aléatoires. *M.R. 21*, p. 975.

[220] DVORETZKY, A., Points of multiplicity c of plane Brownian paths. *M.R* *M.R. 23A*, p. 683.

[221] ____ On the oscillation of the Brownian motion process. *M.R. 29*, p. 334.

[222] DVORETZKY, A. and ERDÖS, P., Divergence of random power series. *M.R. 22*, p. 16.

[223] DVORETSKY, A., ERDOS, P. and KAKUTANI, S., A note on Hausdorff dimension functions. *M.R. 9*, p. 275.

[224] ____ Nonincrease verywhere of the Brownian motion process. *M.R. 24A*, p. 452

[225] DZAGNIDZE, O. P., On universal double series. *M.R. 29*, p. 498.

[226] ____ Representation of measurable functions of two variables by double series. *M.R. 29*, p. 498.

[227] DŽAFARLI, G. M., On the convergence of Fourier series in term of a class of orthonormalized multiplicative systems. *M.R. 26*, p. 104.

[228] DŽVARSEISVILI, A. G., On the convergence of trigonometric series. *M.R. 17*, p. 731.

[229] ____ The Denjoy integral and some questions of analysis. *M.R. 21*, p. 1059.

[230] DYNKIN, E. B., Theory of Markov processes. *M.R. 24A*, p. 322.

[231] EDREI, A., Sur les déterminants récurrents et les singularités d'une fonction donnee par son développement de Taylor. *M.R. 1*, p. 210.

[232] ____ The deficiencies of meromorphic functions of finite lower order. *M.R. 28*, p. 262.

[233] EFIMOV, A. V., On nonsummability of orthogonal series by linear methods. *M.R. 27*, p. 546.

[234] ____ The de la Vallée Poussin summability of orthogonal series. *M.R. 27*, p. 546.

[235] EGGLESTON, H. G., Note on certain s-dimensional sets. *M.R. 11*, p. 166.

[236] ____ Homeomorphisms of s-sets. *M.R. 11*, p. 166.

[237] ____ The Besicovitch dimension of Cartesian product sets. *M.R. 12*, p. 323.

[238] ____ A property of Hausdorff measure. *M.R. 12*, p. 486.

[239] ____ Correction to "A property of Hausdorff measure." *M.R. 13*, p. 121.

[240] ____ A measureless one-dimensional set. *M.R. 15*, p. 943.

[241] ____ A property of bounded analytic functions. *M.R. 17*, p. 599.

[242] ____ The range set of a function meromorphic in the unit circle. *M.R. 17*, p. 957.

[243] ____ The Bohr spectrum of a bounded function. *M.R. 20*, p. 426.

[244] ERDÖS, P., On the convergence of trigonometric series. *M.R. 4*, p. 271.

[245] ____ Some remarks on the measurability of certain sets. *M.R. 7*, p. 197.

[246] ____ Some remarks on polynomials. *M.R. 9*, p. 281.

[247] ERDÖS, P. and JABOTINSKY, E., On analytic iteration. *M.R. 23A*, p. 616.

[248] ERDÖS, P., HERZOG, F. and PIRANIAN, G.„ Metric properites of polynomials. *M.R. 21*, p. 22.

[249] ERDÖS, P. and PIRANIAN, G., Sequences of linear fractional transformations. *M.R. 22*, p. 19.

[250] ERDÖS, P. and TAYLOR, S.J., On the set of points of convergence of a lacunary trigonometric series and the equidistribution properties of related sequences.. *M.R. 19*, pl 1050.

[251] ____ Some problems concerning the structure of random walk paths. *M.R. 22*, p. 2172.

[252] ____ Some intersection properties of random walk paths. *M.R. 23A*, p. 683

[253] ____ On the Hausdorff measure of Brownian paths in the plane. *M.R. 23A*, p. 799.

[254] ____ The Hausdorff measure of the intersection of sets of positive Lebesgue measure. *M.R. 27*, p. 729.

[255] EROHIN, V., The connection between metric dimension and harmonic capacity. *M.R. 21*, p. 146.

[256] EUSTICE, D. J., Non-summable partial sums of orthogonal series. *M.R. 26*, p. 541.

[257] ____ Summability methods and orthogonal series. *M.R. 28*, p. 474.

[258] FEDERER, H., The area of a non-parametric surface. *M.R. 23A*, p. 174.

[259] ____ Currents and area. *M.R. 23A*, p. 175.

[260] FEDULOV, V. S., Generalization of two theorems of A. N. Kolmogorov on lacunary sequences. *M.R. 18*, p. 303.

[261] FEKETE, M., On the semi-continuity of the transfinite diameter. *M.R. 16*, p. 686.

[262] ____ Approximations par polynomes avec conditions diophantiennes. *M.R. 16*, p. 695.

[263] ____ Approximation by polynomials with Diophantine side-conditions. *M.R. 17*, p. 477.

[264] FEKETE, M. and SZEGÖ, G., On algebraic equations with integral coefficients whose roots belong to a given point set. *M.R. 17*, p. 355.

[265] FEKETE, M. and WALSH, J. L., On the asymptotic behavior of polynomials with extremal properties and of their zeros. *M.R. 17*, p. 354.

[266] ____ Asymptotic behavior of restricted extremal polynomials and of their zeros. *M.R. 19*, p. 1045.

[267] FERRAND, J., Sur les fonctions holomorphes on méromorphes dans une couronne. Sur la représentation conforme. *M.R. 4*, p. 138.

[268] FINE, N. J., Cesàro summability of Walsh-Fourier series. *M.R. 17*, p. 31.

[269] FINN, R., Sur quelques généralisations du théorème de Picard. *M.R. 14*, p. 364.

[270] FLEMING, W. H., Functions whose partial derivatives are measures. *M.R. 24A*, p. 35.

[271] FLETT, T. M., Some more theorems concerning the absolute summability of Fourier series and power series. *M.R. 21*, p. 281.

[272] ____ Some theorems on fractional integrals. *M.R. 21*, p. 547.

[273] FRÉCHET, M., Une généralisation de la raréfaction. *M.R. 23A*, p. 48.

[274] FRIEDMAN, A., Entire solutions of partial differential equations with constant coefficients. *M.R. 28*, p. 1016.

[275] FROSTMAN, O., Sur les produits de Blaschke. *M.R. 6*, p. 262.

[276] FUCHS, W. H. J., Proof of a conjecture of G. Pólya concerning gap series. *M.R. 28*, p. 615.

[277] FUGLEDE, B., The symmetric normal derivative of a subharmonic function. *M.R. 22*, p. 981.

[278] ____ On generalized potentials of functions in the Lebesgue classes. *M.R. 28*, p. 441.

[279] FUJIIE, T., A few applications of extremal length. *M.R. 27*, p. 63.

[280] GÁL, I. S., Sur les séries orthogonales C(1)-sommable et $\lambda(n)$-lacunaires. *M.R. 10*, p. 292.

[281] GÁL, S. and GÁL, L., The discrepancy of the sequence $\{(2^n x)\}$. *M.R. 29*, p. 79.

[282] GARABEDIAN, P. R., A problem of Robinson. *M.R. 11*, p. 340.

[283] ____ Schwarz's lemma and the Szegö kernel function. *M.R. 11*, p. 340.

[284] GARG, K. M., An analogue of Denjoy's theorem. *M.R. 26*, p. 492.

[285] ____ On the derivability of functions discontinuous at a dense set. *M.R. 26*, p. 492.

[286] GARSIA, A. M., Existence of almost everywhere convergent rearrangements for Fourier series of L_2 functions. *M.R. 28*, p. 833.

[287] GEFFROY, J., Quelques extensions du théorème de M. Paul Lévy sur la convergence presque sûre des séries aléatoires à termes indépendants. *M.R. 21*, p. 975.

[288] GEHRING, F. W., The boundary behaviour and uniqueness of solutions of the heat equation. *M.R. 22*, p. 472.

[289] ____ The definitions and exceptional sets for quasi-conformal mappings. *M.R. 23A*, p. 332.

[290] ____ On the Dirichlet problem. *M.R.*, *18*, p. 650.

[291] ____ On the radial order of subharmonic functions. *M.R. 19*, p. 131.

[292] GEHRING, F.W. and LEHTO, O., On the total differentiability of functions of a complex variable. *M.R. 23A*, p. 331.

[293] GEHRING, F. W. and VÄISÄLÄ, J., On the geometric definition for quasi-conformal mappings. *M.R. 25*, p. 798.

[294] GERMANSKY, B., On the systems of Fekete-points of an arc of a circumference. *M.R. 10*, p. 523.

[295] ____ On the Fekete-systems of sets consisting of an arbitrary finite number of finite and closed intervals of a straight line. I. *M.R. 14*, p. 854.

[296] GERMEIER, G., Sur les nombres dérivés symétriques. *M.R. 5*, p. 114.

[297] GERONIMUS, J.L., On the character of the solution of the moment-problem in the case of the periodic in the limit associated fraction.1 *M.R. 3*, p. 110.

[298] ____ On some distribution functions connected with systems of polynomials. *M.R. 7*, p. 63.

[299] ____ On certain asymptotic properties of polynomials. *M.R. 10*, p. 190.

[300] ____ On properties of some orthogonal series. *M.R. 17*, p. 257.

[301] ____ On a conjecture of V. A. Steklov. *M.R. 24A*, p. 522.

[302] ____ Some fundamental inequalities in the theory of orthogonal polynomials. *M.R. 24A*, p. 522.

[303] GIERL, A., Über das Hausdorffsche Mass gewisser Punktmengen in der Ziffertheorie. *M.R. 27*, p. 54.

[304] GILLIS, J., Tchebycheff polynomials and the transfinite diameter. *M.R. 2*, p. 282.

[305] GIULIANO, L., Sulle transformazioni assolutamente continue. *M.R. 9*, p. 339.

[306] ____ Alcune proprietà delle transformazioni assolutamente continue. *M.R. 10*, p. 185.

[307] GLADYSZ, S., Ergodische Funktionale und individueller ergodischer Satz. *M.R. 26*, p. 976.

[308] GLIVENKO, E. V., On planar variation. *M.R. 14*, p. 30.

[309] GODEFROID, M., Une propriété des fonctions B.L.D. dans un espace de Green. *M.R. 22*, p. 476.

[310] GOFFMAN, C., On Lebesgue's density theorem. *M.R. 12*, p. 167.

[311] ____ On the approximate limits of a real function. *M.R. 25*, p. 788.

[312] GOLINSKII, B. L., Summation of Fourier-Čebysev series by the Fejér method. *M.R. 21*, p. 687.

[313] ____ On a theorem of Hardy and Littlewood. *M.R. 25*, p. 462.

[314] GOLUSIN, G., On some properties of polynomials. *M.R. 8*, p. 22.

[315] GONČAR, A. A., On series of rational functions. *M.R. 25*, p. 76.

[316] GÓRSKI, J., Sur l'équivalence de deux constructions de la fonction de Green généralisée d'un domaine plan quelconque. *M.R. 10*, p. 296.

[317] ____ Remarque sur le diamètre transfini des ensembles plans. *M.R. 12*, p. 703.

[318] ____ Méthode des points extrémaux de résolution du problème de Dirichlet dans l'espace. *M.R. 17*, p. 604.

[319] ____ Sur certaines propriétés de points extrémaux liés à un domaine plan. *M.R. 18*, p. 730.

[320] ____ On a certain sequence which converges to the generalized transfinite diameter of a plane set. *M.R. 19*, p. 262.

[321] ____ Sur la representation conforme d'un domaine multiplement connexe. *M.R. 20*, p. 562.

[322] ____ Distributions restreintes des points extremaux liés aux ensembles dans l'espace. *M.R. 20*, p. 562.

[323] ____ Limits of a certain functional connected with the capacity of a plane set. *M.R. 26*, p. 62.

[324] GOSSELIN, R. P., On the divergence of Fourier series. *M.R. 20*, p. 425.

[325] ____ On the convergence of Fourier series of functions in an L^p class. *M.R. 18*, p. 303.

[326] ____ On Diophantine approximation and trigonometric polynomials. *M.R. 22*, p. 27.

[327] ____ Some theorems on L^p-Fourier series. *M.R. 22*, p. 480.

[328] ____ Orthonormal series and density of integers. *M.R. 23A*, p. 515.

[329] ____ On the interpolation of L^p functions by Jackson polynomials. *M.R. 24A*, p. 179.

[330] GOWRISANKARAN, K., Limites fines ''à la frontière'' dans la théorie axiomatique du potentiel de M. Brelot. *M.R. 27*, p. 70.

[331] GREEN, J. W., A special type of conformal map. *M.R. 4*, p. 156.

[332] GREPAČEVSKAJA, L. V., On absolute summability by the methods of Cesàro, Riesz and Zygmund. *M.R. 28*, p. 831.

[333] GRÜNWALD, G., Über die Summabilität der Fourierschen Reihe. *M.R. 2*, p. 280.

[334] ____ Eine Bemerkung zu meiner Arbeit ''Über die Summabilität der Fourierschen Reihe''. *M.R. 7*, p. 293.

[335] GUSTIN, W., Boxing inequalities. *M.R. 23A*, p. 174.

[336] HAEGI, H.-R., Sur le maximum du rayon intérieur. *M.R. 10*, p. 534.

[337] HANŠ, O., Almost sure convergence theorem for random Schwartz distributions. *M.R. 21*, p. 1234.

[338] HARDY, G. H. and ROGOSINSKI, W. W., Notes on Fourier series. V. Summability (R_1). *M.R. 10*, p. 528.

[339] HARTMAN, P., On Dirichlet series involving random coefficients. *M.R. 1*, p. 53.

[340] HAVIN, V.P. and HAVINSION, S.J., Some estimates of analytic capacity. *M.R. 24A*, p. 253.

[341] HAVINSON, S. J., On an extremal problem of the theory of analytic functions. *M.R. 11*, p. 508.

[342] ____ The analytic capacity of plane sets, some classes of analytic functions and the extremum function in Schwarz's lemma for arbitrary regions. *M.R. 22*, p. 1628.

[343] _____ The analytic capacity of sets as related to mass distributions. *M.R. 22*, p. 1628.

[344] _____ Approximation on sets of zero analytic capacity. *M.R. 23A*, p. 182.

[345] _____ On approximation with account taken of the size of the coefficients of the approximants. *M.R. 25*, p. 40.

[346] _____ The analytic capacity of sets related to the non-triviality of various classes of analytic functions, and on Schwarz's lemma in arbitrary domains. *M.R. 25*, p. 40.

[347] _____ The radii of univalence, starlikeness and convexity of a class of analytic functions in multiply-connected domains. *M.R. 25*, p. 40.

[348] HAYMAN, W. K., Some applications of the transfinite diameter to the theory of functions. *M.R. 13*, p. 545.

[349] _____ Questions of regularity connected with the Phragmén-Lindelöf principle. *M.R. 17*, p. 1073.

[350] _____ Slowly growing integral and subharmonic functions. *M.R. 22*, p.454.

[351] HEINS, M., Riemann surfaces of infinite genus. *M.R. 13*, p. 643.

[352] _____ Lindelöfian maps. *M.R. 17*, p. 726.

[353] _____ On certain meromorphic functions of bounded valence. *M.R. 20*, p. 290.

[354] _____ On the principle of harmonic measure. *M.R. 21*, p. 1062.

[355] _____ Selected topics in the classical theory of functions of a complex variable. *M.R. 29*, p. 42.

[356] HERSCH, J., Longueurs extrémales, mesure harmonique et distance hyperbolique. *M.R. 14*, p. 262.

[357] HERSCH, J. et PFLUGER, A., Généralisation du lemme de Schwarz et du principe de la mesure harmonique pour les fonctions pseudo-analytiques. *M.R. 13*, p. 736.

[358] HERVÉ, M., A propos d'un mémoire récent de M. Noshiro: Nouvelles applications de sa méthode. *M.R. 14*, p. 460.

[359] _____ Sur les valeurs omises par une fonction méromorphe. *M.R. 16*, p. 684.

[360] _____ Contribution à l'étude d'une fonction méromorphe au voisinage d'un ensemble singulier de capacité nulle. *M.R. 18*, p. 386.

[361] _____ Valeurs exceptionnelles d'une fonction méromorphe au voisinage d'un ensemble singulier de capacité nulle. *M.R. 21*, p. 262.

[362] HERZOG, F. and PIRANIAN, G., Sets of convergence of Taylor series. I. *M.R. 11*, p. 91.

[363] ____ Sets of convergence of Taylor series. II. *M.R. 14*, p. 738.

[364] ____ Sets of radial continuity of analytic functions. *M.R. 16*, p. 231.

[365] ____ Some point sets associated with Taylor series. *M.R. 17*, p. 834.

[366] HINDERER, K., Über die Häufigkeit von Potenzreihen mit vorgegebenen Singularitäten. *M.R. 25*, p. 609.

[367] HIRASAWA, Y., On the bounded solutions of the partial differential equation $\Delta u = f(x, y, u, p, q)$. *M.R. 21*, p. 534.

[368] HONG, I., On some boundary value problem in an annulus. *M.R. 16*, p. 34.

[369] ____ On positively infinite singularities of a solution of the equation $\Delta u + k^2 u = 0$. *M.R. 18*, p. 296.

[370] HOPF, E., On the ergodic theorem for positive linear operators. *M.R. 23A*, p. 615.

[371] HUBER, A., Zum Randverhalten subharmonischer Funktionen. *M.R. 21*, p. 276.

[372] HUGHS, R. E., Functions of BVC type. *M.R. 24A*, p. 248.

[373] HUNT, G. A., Markov chains and Martin boundaries. *M.R. 23A*, p. 119.

[374] HUSKIVADZE, G. A., On *A*-integrals of Cauchy type. *M.R. 26*, p. 979.

[375] AF HÄLLSTRÖM, G., Über meromorphe Funktionen mit mehrfach zusammenhängenden Existenzgebieten. *M.R. 2*, p. 275.

[376] ____ On the conformal mapping of incision domains. *M.R. 14*, p. 549.

[377] ____ Eine Bemerkung über Einschnittgebiete. *M.R. 14*, p. 861.

[378] ____ Eine quasikonforme Abbildung mit Anwendungen auf die Wertverteilungslehre. *M.R. 15*, p. 116.

[379] ____ Kapazitätsbeziehungen bei konformer Abbildung von Einschnittgebieten. *M.R. 15*, p. 208.

[380] ____ Über einige Einschnittgebiete allgemeinerer Art. *M.R. 16*, p. 685.

[381] ____ On the capacity of generalized Cantor sets. *M.R. 17*, p. 146.

[382] ____ Zur Berechnung der Bodenordnung oder Bodenhyperordnung eindeutiger Funktionen. *M.R. 18*, p. 27.

[383] IGARI, S., On multiplicators of orthogonal series. *M.R. 26*, p. 788.

[384] ____ On the decomposition theorems of Fourier transforms with weighted norms. *M.R. 26*, p. 788.

[385] IKEGAMI, T., On Fatou's theorem. *M.R. 26*, p. 748.

[386] IKOMA, K., On a property of the boundary correspondence under quasiconformal mappings. *M.R. 22*, p. 452.

[387] ____ A criterion for a set and its image under quasiconformal mapping to be of $\alpha (0 < \alpha \leq 2)$-dimensional measure zero. *M.R. 28*, p. 616.

[388] INOUE, M., Sur l'approximation des fonctions continues par des fonctions harmoniques (II). *M.R. 1*, p. 230.

[389] ____ On functional determination of the stability of Dirichlet's problem. *M.R. 11*, p. 175.

[390] ____ Sur la détermination fonctionnelle de la solution du problème généralisé de Dirichlet. *M.R. 12*, p. 609.

[391] IONESCU, T. A., Analytic continuation of random series. *M.R. 22*, p. 805.

[392] IONESCU, T. A. and IONESCU, T. C., On the lifting property. III. *M.R. 28*, p. 39.

[393] ITO, J., Asymptotic properties of subharmonic and analytic functions. *M.R. 20*, p. 421.

[394] ____ Properties of subharmonic functions in the half-plane. *M.R. 20*, p. 683.

[395] IVANOV, L. D., On Denjoy's conjecture. *M.R. 28*, p. 51.

[396] ____ Removable singularities of interior mappings. *M.R. 28*, p. 1003.

[397] ____ On the analytic capacity of linear sets. *M.R. 29*, p. 51.

[398] IVAŠEV-MUSATOV, O. S., On trigonometric null-series. *M.R. 18*, p. 803.

[399] ____ On coefficients of trigonometric null-series. *M.R. 20*, p. 894.

[400] ____ *M*-sets and Hausdorff measure. *M.R. 26*, p. 1019.

[401] IZUMI, S., Notes on Fourier analysis. XXI. On the degree of approximation of the partial sums of a Fourier series. *M.R. 12*, p. 174.

[402] ____ Notes on Fourier analysis. XLIV. On the law of the iterated logarithm of some sequences of functions. *M.R. 14*, p. 553.

[403] ____ Notes on Fourier analysis. XVI. On the strong law of large numbers and gap series. *M.R. 14*, p. 868.

[404] ____ Some trigonometrical series. XV. *M.R. 17*, p. 478.

[405] ____ Some trigonometrical series. XVI. *M.R. 17*, p. 608.

[406] ____ Some trigonometrical series. XIX. *M.R. 17*, p. 1079.

[407] ____ Fourier series. III. Wiener's problem. *M.R. 18*, p. 652.

[408] IZUMI, S., SATO, M. and UCHIYAMA, S., Fourier series. XII. Bernstein polynomials. *M.R. 19*, p. 649.

[409] JENKINS, J., Sur quelques aspects globaux du théorème de Picard. *M.R. 17*, p. 725.

[410] ____ Remarks on the paper "Generalization of a theorem of Mandelbrojt". *M.R. 26*, p. 55.

[411] JURCHESCU, M., A maximal Riemann surface. *M.R. 25*, p. 612.

[412] ____ Modulus of a boundary component. *M.R. 21*, p. 389.

[413] JURKAT, W. B., Zur gliedweisen Differentiation fast überall. *M.R. 22*, p. 659.

[414] KAC, M., Convergence and divergence of non-harmonic gap series. *M.R. 3*, p. 107.

[415] ____ Convergence of certain gap series. *M.R. 5*, p. 4.

[416] KAHANE, J. P., Généralisation d'un théorème de S. Bernstein. *M.R. 19*, p. 1050.

[417] ____ Propriétés locales des fonctions à séries de Fourier aléatoires. *M.R. 22*, p. 1408.

[418] ____ Sur la divergence presque sure presque partout de certaines séries de Fourier aléatoires. *M.R. 24A*, p. 522.

[419] ____ Sur les coefficients de Fourier-Bohr. *M.R. 26*, p. 324.

[420] ____ Sur les fonctions presque périodiques generalisées dont le spectre est vide. *M.R. 26*, p. 327.

[421] KAHANE, J.-P. et SALEM, R., Sur les ensembles linéaires ne portant pas de pseudomesures. *M.R. 18*, p. 651.

[422] ____ Sur les ensembles de Carleson et de Helson. *M.R. 19*, p. 31.

[423] ____ Construction de pseudomesures sur les ensembles parfaits symétriques. *M.R. 19*, p. 268.

[424] ____ Distribution modulo 1 and sets of uniqueness. *M.R. 28*, p. 290.

[425] ____ Ensembles parfaits et séries trigonométriques. *M.R. 28*, p. 641.

[426] KAKUTANI, S., Random walk and the type problem of Riemann surfaces. *M.R. 15*, p. 25.

[427] KAMETANI, S., Boundary values of analytic functions. *M.R. 2*, p. 355.

[428] ____ Theorems on interval-functions and h-measures. *M.R. 3*, p. 74.

[429] ____ The exceptional values of functions with the set of linear measure zero, of essential singularities. *M.R. 3*, p. 78.

[430] ____ The exceptional values of functions with the set of capacity zero of essential singularities. *M.R. 7*, p. 380.

[431] ____ The exceptional values of functions with the set of linear measure zero of essential singularities. II. *M.R. 7*, p. 427.

[432] ____ On some properties of Hausdorff's measure and the concept of capacity in generalized potentials. *M.R. 7*, p. 522.

[433] ____ A note on a metric property of capacity. *M.R. 15*, p. 622.

[434] KANIEV, S., On the deviation from their boundary values of functions which are biharmonic in the circle. *M.R. 28*, p. 51.

[435] KANO, S., On the convergence of generalized discrete martingale processes. *M.R. 22*, p. 1459.

[436] KAPLAN, W., On Gross's star theorem, schlicht functions, logarithmic potentials and Fourier series. *M.R. 13*, p. 337.

[437] ____ Extensions of the Gross star theorem. *M.R. 16*, p. 232.

[438] KARLIN, S., Orthogonal properties of independent functions. *M.R. 11*, p. 353.

[439] KATO, Y., The space of bounded solutions and removable singularities of the equation $\Delta u + au_x + bu_y + cu = 0$ $(c \leq 0)$. *M.R. 26*, p. 1002.

[440] KAUFMANN, I., On analytic, uniform, everywhere continuous functions with a perfect and totally discontinuous set of singularities. *M.R. 13*, p. 544.

[441] KAWAKAMI, Y., On Montel's theorem. *M.R. 18*, p. 292.

[442] ____ Theorems on subharmonic functions in the unit circle. *M.R. 19*, p. 262.

[443] KAWATA, T., Notes on Fourier series. XIII. Remarks on the strong summability of Fourier series. *M.R. 7*, p. 247.

[444] KAWATA, T. and UDAGAWA, M., Some gap theorems. *M.R. 12*, p. 175.

[445] KEGEJAN, É. M., On the radial behavior of functions analytic in a circle. *M.R. 28*, p. 1001.

[446] KELDYCH, M. V., On the solubility and the stability of Dirichlet's problem. *M.R. 3*, p. 123.

[447] KELDYCH, M. et LAVRENTIEFF, M., Sur un problème de M. Carleman. *M.R. 2*, p. 82.

[448] KELLERER, H. G., Funktionen auf Produkträumen mit vorgegebenen Marginal-Funktionen. *M.R. 26*, p. 972.

[449] ____ Die Schnittmass-Funktionen messbarer Teilmengen eines Produktraumes. *M.R. 26*, p. 973.

[450] ____ Ein Zerlegungsproblem für Lebesguesche Mengen. *M.R. 26*, p. 973.

[451] KEOGH, F. R., On the convergence of lacunary trigonometric series. *M.R. 24A*, p. 405.

[452] KEOGH, F. R. and PETERSEN, G. M., Riesz summability of subsequences. *M.R. 22*, p. 1918.

[453] KERSHNER, R., The number of circles covering a set. *M.R. 1*, p. 8.

[454] KINNEY, J. R., Boundary behavior of Blaschke products in the unit circle. *M.R. 23A*, p. 478.

[455] ____ Note on a singular function of Minkowski. *M.R. 24A*, p. 34.

[456] ____ The convex hull of plane Brownian motion. *M.R. 26*, p. 157.

[457] ____ Tangential limits of functions of the class S_α. *M.R. 26*, p. 282.

[458] KINNEY, J. R. and PITCHER, T. S., The dimension of the support of a random distribution function. *M.R. 28*, p. 888.

[459] KINUKAWA, M., Some strong summability of Fourier series. *M.R. 17*, p. 1079.

[460] ____ On certain strong summability of a Fourier power series. *M.R. 19*, p. 138.

[461] KISHI, M., Capacities of Borelian sets and the continuity of potentials. *M.R. 20*, p. 422.

[462] ____ Maximum principles in the potential theory. *M.R. 29*, p. 51.

[463] KJELLBERG, B., On integral functions bounded on a given set. *M.R. 14*, p. 965.

[464] KLINE, S. A., On curves of fractional dimensions. *M.R. 8*, p. 19.

[465] KOKSMA, J. F., An arithmetical property of some summable functions. *M.R. 12*, p. 86.

[466] KOKSMA, J. F. and SALEM, R., Uniform distribution and Lebesgue integration. *M.R. 11*, p. 239.

[467] KONSTANTINESCU, K., On the behavior of analytic functions at boundary elements on Riemann surfaces. *M.R. 20*, p. 290.

[468] KORÁNYI, A., On the boundary values of holomorphic functions in wedge domains. *M.R. 27*, p. 514.

[469] KOROVKIN, P. P., Generalization of a theorem of D. F. Egorov. *M.R. 9*, p. 339.

[470] _____ The sets of convergence of series of polynomials. *M.R. 9*, p. 339.

[471] _____ On the growth of polynomials on a set. *M.R. 10*, p. 297.

[472] _____ An extremal problem and divergent functional series. *M.R. 28*, p. 834.

[473] KOZLOV, V. Y., On the distribution of positive and negative values of normal orthogonal functions forming a complete system. *M.R. 10*, p. 451.

[474] KOZLOVCEV, S. G., The connection between the Schwarz derivative and set derivatives. *M.R. 26*, p. 735.

[475] _____ On the structure of measurable functions without an asymptotic derivative. *M.R. 28*, p. 610.

[476] KRÁL, J., A note on the perimeter of the Cartesian product of two sets. *M.R. 24A*, p. 368.

[477] KRÁLIK, D., Untersuchung der Integrale und Derivierten gebrochener Ordnung mit den Methoden der konstruktiven Funktionentheorie. *M.R. 18*, p. 34.

[478] KUBO, T., Hyperbolic transfinite diameter and some theorems on analytic functions in an annulus. *M.R. 21*, p. 659.

[479] KUFAREFF, P. P., On one-parameter families of analytic functions. *M.R. 7*, p. 201.

[480] KUFAREFF, P. P. and SEMUHINA, N. V., On a problem of N. N. Luzin. *M.R. 16*, p. 459.

[481] KUNUGUI, K., Une généralisation des théorèmes de M. M. Picard-Nevanlinna sur les fonctions meromorphes. *M.R. 7*, p. 289.

[482] _____ Etude sur la théorie du potentiel généralisé. *M.R. 12*, p. 410.

[483] KURAMOCHI, Z., On covering surfaces. *M.R. 15*, p. 518.

[484] _____ On covering property of abstract Riemann surfaces. *M.R. 16*, p. 26.

[485] _____ Dirichlet problem on Riemann surfaces. I. Correspondence of boundaries. *M.R. 16*, p. 1012.

[486] _____ On the behavior of analytic functions on abstract Riemann surfaces. *M.R. 17*, p. 26.

[487] _____ An estimation of the measure of linear sets. *M.R. 17*, p. 1191.

[488] _____ Analytic functions in the neighbourhood of the ideal boundary. *M.R. 19*, p. 641.

[489] _____ On the ideal boundaries of abstract Riemann surfaces. *M.R. 20*, p. 540.

[490] ____ Representation of Riemann surfaces. *M.R. 21*, p. 1192.

[491] ____ Cluster sets of analytic functions in open Riemann surfaces with regular matrices I. *M.R. 22*, p. 453.

[492] ____ Correspondence of sets on the boundaries of Riemann surfaces. *M.R. 22*, p. 1896.

[493] KURAMOCHI, Z. and KURODA, T., A note on the set of logarithmic capacity zero. *M.R. 17*, p. 26.

[494] KURODA, T., On the uniform meromorphic functions with the set of capacity zero of essential singularities. *M.R. 14*, p. 740.

[495] ____ A criterion for a set to be of 1-dimensional measure zero. *M.R. 22*, p. 1893.

[496] ____ On some theorems of Sario. *M.R. 22*, p. 1896.

[497] KUSUNOKI, Y., Über die hinreichenden Bedingungen dafür, dass eine Riemannsche Fläche nullberandet ist. *M.R. 14*, p. 550.

[498] ____ Note on the continuation of harmonic and analytic functions. *M.R. 17*, p. 26.

[499] KÖVARI, T., On theorems of G. Pólya and P. Turan. *M.R. 21*, p. 133.

[500] LAMPERTI, J., Criteria for the recurrence or transience of stochastic process. *M.R. 23A*, p. 795.

[501] LANGE, L. H., Sur les cercles de remplissage non-euclidiens. *M.R. 23A*, p. 734.

[502] LATYŠEVA, T. S., On the measure of the values assumed by functions at points where the gradient vanishes. *M.R. 26*, p. 971.

[503] LEHTO, O., On the existence of analytic functions with a finite Dirichlet integral. *M.R. 11*, p. 338.

[504] ____ Sur la théorie des fonctions méromorphes à caractéristique bornée. *M.R. 14*, p. 858.

[505] ____ On meromorphic functions whose values lie in a given domain. *M.R. 15*, p. 517.

[506] ____ On the distribution of values of meromorphic functions of bounded characteristic. *M.R. 15*, p. 947.

[507] ____ On meromorphic functions of bounded characteristic. *M.R. 16*, p. 688.

[508] ____ Value distribution and boundary behavior of a function of bounded characteristic and the Riemann surface of its inverse function. *M.R. 16*, p. 688.

[509] ____ Boundary theorems for analytic functions. *M.R. 17*, p. 472.

[510] ____ On the first boundary value problem for functions harmonic in the unit circle. *M.R. 17*, p. 960.

[511] ____ Distribution of values and singularities of analytic functions. *M.R. 20*, p. 542.

[512] ____ A generalization of Picard's theorem. *M.R. 21*, p. 782.

[513] LEINDLER, L., Bemerkungen zu Sätzen von K. Tandori. *M.R. 25*, p. 1038.

[514] ____ Abschätzungen für die Partialsummen und für die $(R, \lambda(n), 1)$-Mittel allgemeiner Orthogonalreihen. *M.R. 26*, p. 540.

[515] ____ Über die starke Summierbarkeit der Orthogonalreihen. *M.R. 26*, p. 1014.

[516] ____ Über die Rieszschen Mittel allgemeiner Orthogonalreihen. *M.R. 27*, p. 545.

[517] ____ Über unbedingte Konvergenz der Orthogonalreihen mit strukturellen Bedingungen. *M.R. 28*, p. 88.

[518] ____ Über Approximation mit Orthogonalreihenmitteln unter strukturellen Bedingungen. *M.R. 28*, p. 835.

[519] ____ On unconditional convergence of trigonometric series. *M.R. 28*, p. 835.

[520] ____ Unconditional convergence of trigonometrical series. I. *M.R. 29*, p. 295.

[521] LEINDLER, L. und PÁL, L.G., Über die Konvergenz von Partialsummen der Orthogonalreihen. *M.R. 28*, p. 472.

[522] LEJA, F., Sur les suites de polynomes et la fonction de Green généralisée. *M.R. 8*, p. 255.

[523] ____ Sur les polynomes de Tchebycheff et la fonction de Green. *M.R. 9*, p. 183.

[524] ____ Sur le domaine de convergence des séries de polynomes homogènes à deux variables. *M.R. 10*, p. 111.

[525] ____ Une généralisation de l'écart et du diamètre transfini d'un ensemble. *M.R. 11*, p. 717.

[526] ____ Une méthode d'approximation des fonctions réelles d'une variable complexe. *M.R. 12*, p. 609.

[527] ____ Sur les coefficients des fonctions analytiques univalentes dans le cercle et les points extremaux des ensembles. *M.R. 12*, p. 691.

[528] ____ Une méthode élémentaire de résolution du problème de Dirichlet dans le plan. *M.R. 12*, p. 703.

[529] ____ Construction of the function mapping conformally an arbitrary simply connected domain upon a circle. *M.R. 16*, p. 917.

[530] ____ Propriétés des points extrémaux des ensembles plans et leur application à la représentation conforme. *M.R. 19*, p. 645.

[531] ____ Points extrémaux des ensembles et leur application dans la théorie des fonctions. *M.R. 20*, p. 539.

[532] ____ Distributions libres et restreintes des points extrémaux dans les ensembles plans. *M.R. 20*, p. 561.

[533] LELONG, J., Propriétés des fonctions subharmoniques positives dans un demiespace. Quelques applications de la théorie du potentiel. Distributions capacitaires pour les potentiels de fonction de Green. *M.R. 10*, p. 39.

[534] LELONG, P., Sur les zéros d'une fonction entière de deux variables. *M.R. 3*, p. 84.

[535] ____ Sur la capacité de certains ensembles de valeurs exceptionnelles. *M.R. 5*, p. 177.

[536] LÉVINE, B. and LIFSCHETZ, M., Quasi-analytic functions represented by Fourier series. *M.R. 3*, p. 106.

[537] LIBERMAN, J., Théorème de Denjoy sur la dérivée d'une fonction arbitraire par rapport à une fonction continue. *M.R. 3*, p. 74.

[538] LIBOUBAN, J.-L. et RIEU, N., Sur un problème de K. Urbanik concernant la dimension de Hausdorff. *M.R. 26*, p. 1201.

[539] LITTMAN, W., A strong maximum principle for weakly L-subharmonic functions. *M.R. 21*, p. 1200.

[540] LITTMAN, W. and STAMPACCHIA, G. and WEINBERGER, H. F., Regular points for elliptic equations with discontinuous coefficients. *M.R. 28*, p. 821.

[541] LIVSIC, M. I., Uniqueness of a trigonometrical series expansion for summability methods. *M.R. 29*, p. 297.

[542] LOEWNER, C., On the conformal capacity in space. *M.R. 21*, p. 657.

[543] LOHWATER, A. J., A uniqueness theorem for a class of harmonic functions. *M.R. 13*, p. 743.

[544] ____ The boundary values of a class of meromorphic functions. *M.R. 14*, p. 34.

[545] ____ The boundary behaviour of a quasi-conformal mapping. *M.R. 18*, p. 26.

[546] ____ Sur le principe de symétrie et la repartition des valeurs des fonctions analytiques bornées. *M.R. 18*, p. 28.

[547] ____ The boundary behaviour of meromorphic functions. *M.R. 20*, p. 663.

[548] ____ The cluster sets of meromorphic functions. *M.R. 21*, p. 927.

[549] ____ The exceptional values of meromorphic functions. *M.R. 22*, p. 455.

[550] ____ On the theorems of Gross and Iversen. *M.R. 23A*, p. 181.

[551] LOHWATER, A. J. and PIRANIAN, G., Conformal mapping of a Jordan region whose boundary has positive two-dimensional measure. *M.R. 14*, p. 262.

[552] ____ On the derivative of a univalent function. *M.R. 15*, p. 114.

[553] ____ On a conjecture of Lusin. *M.R. 17*, p. 834.

[554] ____ The sets of ambiguous points of functions of bounded characteristic. *M.R. 18*, p. 728.

[555] ____ The boundary behaviour of functions analytic in a disk. *M.R. 19*, p. 950.

[556] LOHWATER, A. J., PIRANIAN, G. and RUDIN, W., The derivative of a schlicht function. *M.R. 17*, p. 249.

[557] LOHWATER, A. J. and SEIDEL, W., An example in conformal mapping. *M.R. 9*, p. 420.

[558] LOJASIEWICZ, S., Théorème de Fatou pour les équations elliptiques. *M.R. 28*, p. 458.

[559] LOKKI, O., Beiträge zur Theorie der analytischen und harmonischen Funktionen mit endlichem Dirichlet-integral. *M.R. 13*, p. 338.

[560] ____ Über analytische Funktionen mit gegebenen Randwerten. *M.R. 17*, p. 725.

[561] LOOMIS, L. H., A note on the Hilbert transform. *M.R. 8*, p. 377.

[562] LOVATOR, A. DZ., On the theorems of Gross and Iversen. *M.R. 21*, p. 1194.

[563] LUMER-NAIM, L., Sur le théorème de Fatou généralisé. *M.R. 25*, p. 433

[564] LUXEMBURG, W. A. J., Addendum to "On the measurability of a function which occurs in a paper by A. C. Zaanen". *M.R. 28*, p. 255.

[565] MACLANE, G. R. and RYAN, F. B., On the radial limits of Blaschke products. *M.R. 26*, p. 503.

[566] MANDELBROJT, S., Généralisation d'un théorème de S. Bernstein concernant les fonctions entières de type exponentiel. *M.R. 27*, p. 936.

[567] MARCINKIEWICZ, J., Sur une nouvelle condition pour la convergence presque partout des séries de Fourier. *M.R. 1*, p. 329.

[568] MARCINKIEWICZ, J. and ZYGMUND, A., On the behaviour of trigonometric series and power series. *M.R. 3*, p. 105.

[569] MARCUS, S., Sur un problème de F. Hausdorff concernant les fonctions symétriques continues. *M.R. 18*, p. 23.

[570] _____ Points of discontinuity and points of differentiability. *M.R. 20*, p. 656.

[571] _____ Sur les fonctions dérivées, intégrables au sens de Riemann et sur les dérivées partielles mixtes. *M.R. 21*, p. 385.

[572] _____ Sur un théorème de F. B. Jones. Sur un théorème de S. Kurepa. *M.R. 21*, p. 513.

[573] _____ Functions with the Darboux property and functions with connected graphs. *M.R. 22*, p. 1890.

[574] _____ Les ensembles stationnaires de certaines classes de fonctions derivées. *M.R. 26*, p. 492.

[575] _____ Points of discontinuity and points at which the derivative is infinite. *M.R. 26*, p. 492.

[576] _____ Sur une généralisation de la notion de quasi-analyticité. *M.R. 26*, p. 492.

[577] _____ Zusammensetzung von Funktionen von beschränkter Variation. *M.R. 26*, p. 735.

[578] MARSTRAND, J. M., The dimension of Cartesian product sets. *M.R. 15* p. 691.

[579] _____ Some fundamental geometrical properties of plane sets of fraction dimensions. *M.R. 16*, p. 121.

[580] _____ Hausdorff two-dimensional measure in 3-space. *M.R. 23A*, p. 172.

[581] MARTIN, N. F. G., A topology for certain measure spaces. *M.R. 28*, p. 996.

[582] MARUYAMA, G., Summability of Fourier series. *M.R. 2*, p. 279.

[583] MATSUMOTO, K., On subsurfaces of some Riemann surfaces. *M.R. 21*, p. 1192.

[584] ____ Exceptional values of meromorphic functions in a neighbourhood of the set of singularities. *M.R. 24A*, p. 41.

[585] ____ On exceptional values of meromorphic functions with the set of singularities of capacity zero. *M.R. 24A*, p. 41.

[586] ____ On a theorem of cluster sets. *M.R. 28*, p. 48.

[587] MATSUMURA, Y., Note on the summability of orthogonal series. *M.R. 15*, p. 119.

[588] MATSUYAMA, N., On the convergence of some gap series. *M.R. 21*, p. 280.

[589] MATSUYAMA, N. and TAKAHASHI, S., On the gap sequence having random signs. *M.R. 21*, p. 280.

[590] ____ The law of the iterated logarithms. *M.R. 25*, p. 837.

[591] MAUDE, R., Exceptional sets with respect to order of integral functions of two variables. *M.R. 19*, p. 402.

[592] ____ Conditions for positive Φ-capacity. *M.R. 26*, p. 984.

[593] MAZUR, S. et ORLICZ, W., Sur quelques propriétés de fonctions périodiques et presque-périodiques. *M.R. 3*, p. 107.

[594] MEDER, J., On the estimation of Cesàro means of orthonormal series. *M.R. 19*, p. 1174.

[595] ____ On the strong summability of orthogonal series. *M.R. 23A*, p. 646.

[596] ____ On the estimation of $(\overline{N}, p_n)$-means of orthogonal series. *M.R. 24A*, p. 66.

[597] ____ On very strong Riesz-summability of orthogonal series. *M.R. 24A*, p. 282.

[598] ____ On the summability almost everywhere of orthonormal series by the method of Euler-Knopp. *M.R. 24A*, p. 283.

[599] ____ On the Nörlund summability of orthogonal series. *M.R. 26*, p. 535.

[600] MEIER, K., Über die Randwerte meromorpher Funktionen und hinreichende Bedingungen für Regularität von Funktionen einer komplexen Variablen. *M.R. 12*, p. 490.

[601] ____ Über Mengen von Randwerten meromorpher Funktionen. *M.R. 17*, p. 956.

[602] MENŠOV, D.E., Sur la convergence uniforme des séries de Fourier. *M.R. 3*, p. 106.

[603] ____ Sur la représentation des fonctions mesurables par des séries trigonométriques. *M.R. 3*, p. 106.

[604] ____ Sur les séries trigonométriques universelles. *M.R. 7*, p. 435.

[605] ____ On the Fourier series of continuous and summable functions. *M.R. 11*, p. 26.

[606] ____ On the limits of indeterminateness of trigonometric series. *M.R. 12*, p. 255.

[607] ____ On limits of indeterminacy of Fourier series. *M.R. 14*, p. 40.

[608] ____ On the limits of indetermination of partial sums of universal trigonometric series. *M.R. 16*, p. 467.

[609] ____ On limit functions of a trigonometrical series. *M.R. 21*, p. 414.

[610] ____ On convergent sequences of partial sums of a trigonometric series. *M.R. 22*, p. 663.

[611] ____ On the summation of orthogonal series by linear methods. *M.R. 22*, p. 1401.

[612] ____ Summability of orthogonal series by linear methods. *M.R. 25*, p. 1039.

[613] ____ On the limits of indeterminacy of subsequences of partial sums of Fourier series. *M.R. 26*, p. 324.

[614] MERGELYAN, S. N., On best approximation on closed sets. *M.R. 10*, p. 243.

[615] ____ Certain classes of sets and their applications. *M.R. 24A*, p. 258.

[616] MEYER, P. A., Decomposition of supermartingales: the uniqueness theorem. *M.R. 26*, p. 372.

[617] MICHAEL, J.H., The convergence of measures on parametric surfaces. *M.R. 26*, p. 741.

[618] MIESNER, W., Sätze zur absoluten Summierung von Laplace-Stieltjes Integralen. *M.R. 29*, p. 81.

[619] MILLOUX, H., Les fonctions méromorphes et leurs dérivées. Extensions d'un théorème de M. R. Nevanlinna. Applications. *M.R. 7*, p. 427.

[620] MITCHELL, J., On double Sturm-Liouville series. *M.R. 5*, p. 96.

[621] _____ Convergence and (*C*, 1, 1) summability of double orthogonal series. *M.R. 12*, p. 698.

[622] MIZUMOTO, H., On Riemann surfaces with finite spherical area. *M.R. 19*, p. 1044.

[623] _____ A note on an Abelian covering surface. *M.R. 27*, p. 61.

[624] MOCANU, G. et BOBOC, N., Sur la propriété (*N*) de Menchov. *M.R. 24A*, p. 606.

[625] MONTEL, P., Sur les valeurs algébriques des fonctions analytiques. *M.R. 20*, p. 771.

[626] MORAN, P. A. P., On plane sets of fractional dimensions. *M.R. 11*, p. 17.

[627] _____ The translations of linear sets of fractional dimensions. *M.R. 16*, p. 228.

[628] MORGENTHALER, G. W., On Walsh-Fourier series. *M.R. 19*, p. 956.

[629] MORI, A., On a conformal mapping with certain boundary correspondences. *M.R. 12*, p. 601.

[630] _____ On the existence of harmonic functions on a Rieman surface. *M.R. 13*, p. 735.

[631] _____ On Riemann surfaces, on which no bounded harmonic function exists. *M.R. 14*, p. 367.

[632] _____ An imbedding theorem on finite covering surfaces of the Riemann sphere. *M.R. 15*, p. 615.

[633] _____ On quasi-conformality and pseudo-analyticity. *M.R. 18*, p. 646.

[634] MORIC, F., On unconditional convergence of series in terms of a Haar system. *M.R. 28*, p. 290.

[635] MÓRICZ, F., Über die Rieszsche Summation der Orthogonalreihen. *M.R. 26*, p. 1014.

[636] MORSE, A. P., On intervals of prescribed lengths. *M.R. 16*, p. 22.

[637] MORSE, A. and RANDOLPH, J., Gillespie measure. *M.R. 1*, p. 304.

[638] MONNA, A. F., Sur la capacité des ensembles. *M.R. 1*, p. 238.

[639] MURRAY, F. J., Nullifying functions. *M.R. 2*, p. 131.

[640] MYRBERG, L., Über reguläre und irreguläre Randpunkte des harmonischen Masses. *M.R. 13*, p. 130.

[641] _____ Über die vermischte Randwertaufgabe der harmonischen Funktionen. *M.R. 13*, p. 743.

[642] ____ Bemerkungen zur Theorie der harmonischen Funktionen. *M.R. 13*, p. 743.

[643] ____ Über die Existenz von positiven harmonischen Funktionen auf Riemannschen Flächen. *M.R. 14*, p. 979.

[644] ____ Über die Existenz von positiven harmonischen Funktionen auf offenen Riemannschen Flächen. *M.R. 16*, p. 471.

[645] ____ Über das Dirichletsche Problem auf offenen Riemannschen Flächen. *M.R. 17*, p. 726.

[646] ____ Über meromorphe Funktionen auf endlich vielblättrigen Riemannschen Flächer. *M.R. 28*, p. 260.

[647] MYRBERG, P. J., Über den Fundamentalbereich der automorphen Funktionen. *M.R. 7*, p. 380.

[648] ____ Die Kapazität der singulären Menge der linearen Gruppen. *M.R. 7*, p. 516.

[649] ____ Über die Existenz von beschränktartigen automorphen Funktionen. *M.R. 12*, p. 403.

[650] NACHBIN, L., On almost everywhere divergent series of functions. *M.R. 5*, p. 117.

[651] NAGURA, S., Kernel functions on Riemann surfaces. *M.R. 13*, p. 547.

[652] NAKAI, M., Genus and classifications of Riemann surfaces. *M.R. 25*, p. 797.

[653] NEHARI, Z., Sur la conjuguée d'une fonction harmonique bornée. *M.R. 12*, p. 825.

[654] NEUGEBAUER, C. J., A theorem on derivates. *M.R. 25*, p. 788.

[655] ____ Symmetric, continuous, and smooth functions. *M.R. 28*, p. 253.

[656] NEVANLINNA, R., Sur l'existence de certaines classes de différentielles analytiques. *M.R. 11*, p. 341.

[657] ____ Über Mittelwerte von Potentialfunktionen. *M.R. 11*, p. 516.

[658] ____ Über die Existenz von beschränkten Potentialfunktionen auf Flächen von unendlichem Geschlecht. *M.R. 12*, p. 493.

[659] ____ Bemerkungen zur Lösbarkeit der ersten Randwertaufgabe der Potentialtheorie auf allgemeinen Flächen. *M.R. 13*, p. 36.

[660] ____ Surfaces de Riemann ouvertes. *M.R. 13*, p. 547.

[661] ____ Ein Satz über offene Riemannsche Flächen. *M.R. 2*, p. 85.

[662] NEVEU, J., Sur le théorème ergodique ponctuel. *M.R. 23A*, p. 49.

[663] NEWELL, G. F., Distribution for the smallest distance between any pair of kth nearest neighbor random points on a line. *M.R. 26*, p. 1329.

[664] NEWMAN, D. J., The closure of translates in l^p. *M.R. 29*, p. 296.

[665] NICKEL, P. A., On extremal properties for annular radial and circular slit mappings of bordered Riemann surfaces. *M.R. 25*, p. 41.

[666] NIKOLSKII, S. M., On the Dirichlet problem. *M.R. 13*, p. 943.

[667] ____ On the Dirichlet problem for the circle and half-space. *M.R. 16*, p. 589.

[668] NINOMIYA, N., Sur une suite convergente de distributions de masses et leurs potentiels correspondants. *M.R. 14*, p. 469.

[669] ____ Une correction sur mon travail: "Sur l'intégrale d'énergie dans la théorie du potentiel". *M.R. 17*, p. 1197.

[670] ____ Sur le théorème du balayage et le théorème d'équilibre. *M.R. 17*, p. 1198.

[671] NOSHIRO, K., Contributions to the theory of the singularities of analytic functions. *M.R. 11*, p. 428.

[672] ____ Note on the cluster sets of analytic functions. *M.R. 13*, p. 224.

[673] ____ Open Riemann surface with null boundary. *M.R. 13*, p. 833.

[674] ____ Cluster sets of functions meromorphic in the unit circle. *M.R. 17*, p. 143.

[675] ____ Cluster sets. *M.R. 24A*, p. 614.

[676] NOZAKI, Y., On generalized transfinite diameter. *M.R. 12*, p. 323.

[677] OFFORD, A. C., Approximations to functions by trigonometric polynomials. II. *M.R. 10*, p. 248.

[678] OGUZTÖREL, N., Extension de la théorie de Nevanlinna aux domaines multiplement connexes. *M.R. 17*, p. 357.

[679] OHTSUKA, M., Note on functions bounded and analytic in the unit circle. *M.R. 16*, p. 25.

[680] ____ On exceptional values of a meromorphic function. *M.R. 17*, p. 357.

[681] ____ Théorèmes étoiles de Gross et leurs applications. *M.R. 17*, p. 1191.

[682] ____ On boundary values of an analytic transformation of a circle into a Riemann surface. *M.R. 18*, p. 292.

[683] ____ Capacité d'ensembles de Cantor généralisés. *M.R. 19*, p. 541.

[684] ____ On boundary cluster sets of functions analytic in the unit circle. *M.R. 20*, p. 291.

[685] ____ Capacité des ensembles produits. *M.R. 21*, p. 794.

[686] OLEVSKII, A. M., Unconditional summability of functional series. *M.R. 24A*, p. 66.

[687] ____ Divergent Fourier series of continuous functions. *M.R. 24A*, p. 521.

[688] ____ Divergent series for complete systems in L^2. *M.R. 24A*, p. 521.

[689] ____ Orthogonal series in terms of complete systems. *M.R. 26*, p. 787.

[690] ____ Divergent Fourier series. *M.R. 26*, p. 1019.

[691] ____ The divergence of orthogonal series and the Fourier coefficients of continuous functions with respect to complete systems. *M.R. 27*, p. 969.

[692] ORLICZ, W., On a class of asymptotically divergent sequences of functions. *M.R. 13*, p. 936.

[693] OSSICINI, A., Sulla sommabilità delle serie di Legendre. *M.R. 13*, p. 457.

[694] OSTROVSKII, I. V., On meromorphic functions taking certain values at points lying near a finite system of rays. *M.R. 21*, p. 24.

[695] OSTROW, E. H. and STEIN, E. M., A generalization of lemmas of Marcinkiewicz and Fine with applications to singular integrals. *M.R. 21*, p. 52.

[696] OZAWA, M., On classification of the function-theoretic null-sets on Riemann surfaces of infinite genus. *M.R. 13*, p. 547.

[697] ____ Classification of Riemann surfaces. *M.R. 14*, p. 462.

[698] ____ Remarks on Mr. Ullemar's second harmonic measure. *M.R. 15*, p. 309.

[699] ____ On Riemann surfaces admitting an infinite cyclic conformal transformation group. *M.R. 19*, p. 259.

[700] ____ A set of capacity zero and the equation $\Delta u = Pu$. *M.R. 22*, p. 1626.

[701] ____ A supplement to "On Pfluger's sufficient condition for a set to be of class $N_{\mathfrak{B}}$". *M.R. 25*, p. 428.

[702] OZAWA, M. and KURODA, T., On Pfluger's sufficient condition for a set to be of class $N_{\mathfrak{B}}$. *M.R. 25*, p. 427.

[703] PARREAU, M., Sur les moyennes des fonctions harmoniques et la classification des surfaces de Riemann. *M.R. 12*, p. 259.

[704] ____ Sur les moyennes des fonctions harmoniques et analytiques et la classification des surfaces de Riemann.. *M.R. 14*, p. 263.

[705] ____ Théorème de Fatou et problème de Dirichlet pour les lignes de Green de certaines surfaces de Riemann. *M.R. 20*, p. 769.

[706] PARRY, W., Note on the ergodic theorem of Hurewicz. *M.R. 29*, p. 457.

[707] PEREVALOV, G. E., On the measure of sets lying on plane continua. *M.R. 25*, p. 423.

[708] PERRY, R. L., The zeros of a family of integral functions. *M.R. 19*, p. 400.

[709] PESIN, I.N., Metric properties of *Q*-quasiconformal mappings. *M.R. 19*, p. 258.

[710] PETROVSKAJA, M. B., Null series with respect to a Haar system and sets of uniqueness. *M.R. 29*, p. 504.

[711] PFLUGER, A., Die Wertverteilung und das Verhalten von Betrag und Argument einer speziellen Klasse analytischer Funktionen. II. *M.R. 1*, p. 113.

[712] ____ Une propriété métrique de la représentation quasiconforme. *M.R. 9*, p. 421.

[713] ____ Sur l'existence de fonctions non constantes, analytiques, uniformes et bornées sur une surface de Riemann ouverte.1*M.R.11*, p. 342. *11*, p. 342.

[714] ____ Quasikonforme Abbildungen und logarithmische Kapazität. *M.R. 13*, p. 453.

[715] ____ Extremallängen und Kapazität. *M.R. 16*, p. 810.

[716] ____ Theorie der Riemannschen Flächen. *M.R. 18*, p. 796.

[717] PIRANIAN, G., On a problem of Lohwater. *M.R. 21*, p. 927.

[718] PIRANIAN, G. and RUDIN, W., Lusin's theorem on areas of conformal maps. *M.R. 18*, p. 726.

[719] PIRANIAN, G. and SHIELDS, A., The sets of Lusin points of analytic functions. *M.R. 18*, p. 726.

[720] PIRANIAN, G. and THRON, W. J., Convergence properties of sequences of linear fractional transformations. *M.R. 20*, p. 18.

[721] DU PLESSIS, N., A theorem about fractional integrals. *M.R. 14*, p.546.

[722] ____ Some theorems about the Riesz fractional integral. Spherical fractional integrals. *M.R. 19*, p. 270 and 271.

[723] POMMERENKE, C., Über die analytische Kapazität. *M.R. 22*, p. 963.

[724] ____ Über die Kapazität der Summe von Kontinuen. *M.R. 22*, p. 963.

[725] ____ Über die Kapazität ebener Kontinuen. *M.R. 22*, p. 963.

[726] ____ Einige Sätze über die Kapazität ebener Mengen. *M.R. 22*, p. 1916.

[727] ____ On the capacity of plane sets. *M.R. 24A*, p. 37.

[728] ____ Zwei Bemerkungen zur Kapazität ebener Kontinuen. *M.R. 25*, p. 48.

[729] ____ On hyperbolic capacity and hyperbolic length. *M.R. 26*, p. 1208.

[730] ____ On metric properties of complex polynomials. *M.R. 27*, p. 310.

[731] ____ On the hyperbolic capacity and conformal mapping. *M.R. 27*, p. 1123

[732] POP-STOJANOVIĆ, Z., On the strong law of large numbers. *M.R. 25*, p. 888.

[733] POTYAGAILO, D. B., On the set of boundary values of meromorphic functions. *M.R. 14*, p. 549.

[734] PYATECKII-SAPIRO, I. I., Supplement to the work "On the problem of uniqueness of expansion of a function in a trigonometric series". *M.R. 16*, p. 691.

[735] RANGA RAO, R. and VARADARAJAN, V. S., A limit theorem for densities. *M.R. 24A*, p. 320.

[736] RAVETZ, J., The Denjoy theorem and sets of fractional dimension. *M.R. 15*, p. 298.

[737] RAY, D., Sojourn times and exact Hausdorff measure of the sample path for planar Brownian motion. *M.R. 26*, p. 607.

[738] RÉGNIER, A., Quelques théorèmes ergodiques ponctuces. *M.R. 22*, p. 1372.

[739] REICH, E., A counterexample of Koebe's for slit mappings. *M.R. 26*, p. 498.

[740] RÉNYI, A., On the measure of equidistribution of point sets. *M.R. 11*, p. 647.

[741] RIDDER, J., Erweiterung eines von Montel und Tolstov herrührenden Satzes. *M.R. 28*, p. 432.

[742] ____ Hinreichende Bedingungen für die Analytizität komplexwertiger Funktionen. *M.R. 28*, p. 614.

[743] ROBERTS, G. T., Order continuous measures. *M.R. 28*, p. 791.

[744] ROGERS, C. A., Sets non-σ-finite for Hausdorff measures. *M.R. 26*, p. 738.

[745] ____ Some sets of continued fractions. *M.R. 28*, p. 285.

[746] ROGERS, C. A. and TAYLOR, S. J., Functions continuous and singular with respect to a Hausdorff measure. *M.R. 24A*, p. 35.

[747] ROMANO, A., Sul teorema di Jordan per le serie doppie di Fourier. *M.R. 7*, p. 436.

[748] ROONEY, P. G., On an inversion operator for the Fourier transformation. *M.R. 28*, p. 474.

[749] ROTA, G.-C., On the maximal ergodic theorem for Abel-limits. *M.R. 28*, p. 40.

[750] ROYDEN, H. L., Some remarks on open Riemann surfaces. *M.R. 13*, p. 339.

[751] ____ Harmonic functions on open Riemann surfaces. *M.R. 14*, p. 167.

[752] ____ Some counterexamples in the classification of open Riemann surfaces. *M.R. 14*, p. 864.

[753] ____ A property of quasi-conformal mapping. *M.R. 15*, p. 695.

[754] ____ On a class of null-bounded Riemann surfaces. *M.R. 22*, p. 292.

[755] ____ A generalization of Morera's theorem. *M.R. 25*, p. 1001.

[756] RUBEL, L. A., Differentiability of monotonic functions. *M.R. 27*, p. 930.

[757] RUDIN, W., Uniqueness theory for Hermite series. *M.R. 12*, p. 697.

[758] ____ Analytic functions of class H_p. *M.R. 16*, p. 810.

[759] ____ On a problem of Collingwood and Cartwright. *M.R. 16*, p. 916.

[760] ____ The radial variation of analytic functions. *M.R. 18*, p. 27.

[761] ____ Boundary values of continuous analytic functions. *M.R. 18*, p. 472.

[762] ____ Laplace series and sets of logarithmic capacity zero. *M.R. 19*, p. 410.

[763] ____ Fourier-Stieltjes transforms of measures on independent sets. *M.R. 22*, p. 1669.

[764] ____ Fourier analysis on groups. *M.R. 27*, p. 548.

[765] ____ Essential boundary points. *M.R. 28*, p. 618.

[766] RÜBER, Å., Über die Kapazität einer verallgemeinerten Cantorschen Punktmenge. *M.R. 20*, p. 32.

[767] ____ Über meromorphe Funktionen mit einem Existenzgebiete, dessen Rand eine Cantorsche Punktmenge von der Kapazität null ist. *M.R. 18*, p. 28.

[768] RUNG, D. C., Results on the order of holomorphic functions defined in the unit disk. *M.R. 25*, p. 1004.

[769] ____ Boundary behavior of normal functions defined in the unit disk. *M.R. 26*, p. 1216.

[770] SAFEEV, M. N., Boundary properties of the S_p integral. *M.R. 29*, p. 50.

[771] SAFRONOVA, G. P., Some boundary properties of analytic functions. *M.R. 23A*, p. 478.

[772] SAGATELAN, W. W., Sur l'intégrale du type de Cauchy-Stieltjes à limites infinies. *M.R. 7*, p. 201.

[773] SAGAWA, A., A note on a Riemann surface with null boundary. *M.R. 13*, p. 931.

[774] ____ On the existence of harmonic functions on a Riemann surface. *M.R. 27*, p. 935.

[775] SALÁT, T., Über einen Satz von A. Chincin. *M.R. 26*, p. 534.

[776] ____ Hausdorff measure of linear sets. *M.R. 27*, p. 729.

[777] SALEM, R., Essais sur les séries trigonometriques. *M.R. 2*, p. 93.

[778] ____ The absolute convergence of trigonometrical series. *M.R. 2*, p. 360.

[779] ____ On some properties of symmetrical perfect sets. *M.R. 3*, p. 105.

[780] ____ On sets of multiplicity for trigonometrical series. *M.R. 4*, p. 38.

[781] ____ On singular monotonic functions of the Cantor type. *M.R. 4*, p. 38.

[782] ____ Sets of uniqueness and sets of multiplicity. *M.R. 5*, p. 3.

[783] ____ Sets of uniqueness and sets of multiplicity. II. *M.R. 6*, p. 47.

[784] ____ Sur les sommes Riemanniennes des fonctions sommables. *M.R. 10*, p. 360.

[785] ____ On singular monotonic functions whose spectrum has a given Hausdorff dimension. *M.R. 13*, p. 230.

[786] ____ Uniform distribution and capacity of sets. *M.R. 16*, p. 804.

[787] ____ New theorems on the convergence of Fourier series. *M.R. 17*, p. 845.

[788] ____ On monotonic functions whose spectrum is a Cantor set with constant ratio of dissection. *M.R. 18*, p. 23.

[789] ____ Recherches récentes sur l'unicité du developpement trigonométrique. *M.R. 21*, p. 149.

[790] SALEM, R. and ZYGMUND, A., Capacity of sets and Fourier series. *M.R. 7*, p. 434.

[791] ____ La loi du logarithme itéré pour les séries trigonométriques lacunaires. *M.R. 12*, p. 605.

[792] ____ Sur les séries trigonométriques dont les coefficients ont des signes aléatoires. *M.R. 14*, p. 1081.

[793] ____ Some properties of trigonometric series whose terms have random signs. *M.R. 16*, p. 467.

[794] R. SALINAS, B., Complement to a theorem of Ahlfors-Heins on subharmonic functions. *M.R. 17*, p. 1197.

[795] SAMUELSSON, Å., On the boundary behavior of the derivative of analytic functions. *M.R. 23A*, p. 734.

[796] SARIO, L., Über Riemannsche Flächen mit hebbarem Rand. *M.R. 10*, p. 365.

[797] ____ Existence des fonctions d'allure donnée sur une surface de Riemann arbitraire. *M.R. 11*, p. 342.

[798] ____ Quelques propriétés à la frontière se rattachant à la classification des surfaces de Riemann. *M.R. 11*, p. 342.

[799] ____ Sur la classification des surfaces de Riemann. *M.R. 14*, p. 863.

[800] ____ An extremal method on arbitrary Riemann surfaces. *M.R. 14*, p. 863.

[801] ____ Alternating method on arbitrary Riemann surfaces. *M.R. 15*, p. 209.

[802] ____ Construction of functions with prescribed properties on Riemann surfaces. *M.R. 15*, p. 209.

[803] ____ Capacity of the boundary and of a boundary component. *M.R. 15*, p. 518.

[804] SATO, M., Uniform convergence of Fourier series. V. *M.R. 17*, p. 845.

[805] SATO, T., Sur le problème de Dirichlet généralisé pour l'équation $\Delta u = f(P,u,\partial u)$. *M.R. 25*, p. 823.

[806] SCALORA, F. S., Abstract martingale convergence theorems. *M.R. 23A*, p. 118.

[807] SCERBINA, A. D., On a summation method of series conjugate to Fourier series. *M.R. 12*, p. 329.

[808] SCHAEFFER, A. C., Entire functions and trigonometric polynomials. *M.R. 14*, p. 631.

[809] SCHIFFER, M., On the subadditivity of the transfinite diameter. *M.R. 3*, p. 73.

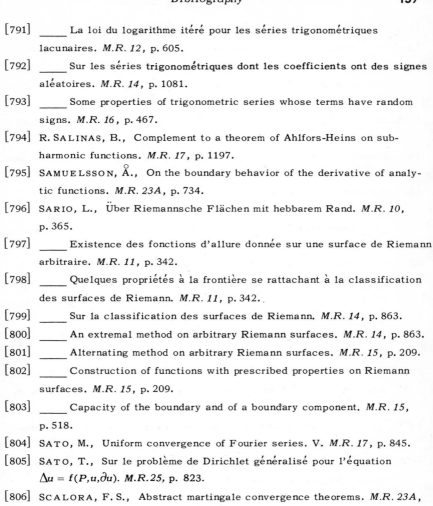

[810] ____ Sur la variation du diamètre transfini. *M.R.4*, p. 78.

[811] ____ Hadamard's formula and variation of domain-functions. *M.R. 8*, p. 325.

[812] SCILARD, K. S., Extension of the Fatou theorem to a class of continuous mappings. *M.R. 21*, p. 1347.

[813] SERRIN, J., On the differentiability of functions of several variables. *M.R. 25*, p. 605.

[814] SHAH, T., On the mapping radii and Green functions of non-overlapping domains. *M.R. 18*, p. 122.

[815] SHAPIRO, V., An extension of results in the uniqueness theory of double trigonometric series. *M.R. 15*, p. 306.

[816] ____ Logarithmic capacity of sets and double trigonometric series. *M.R. 16*, p. 242.

[817] ____ The Laplacian of Fourier transforms. *M.R. 17*, p. 259.

[818] ____ Cantor-type uniqueness of multiple trigonometric integrals. *M.R. 17*, p. 845.

[819] ____ Generalized Laplacians. *M.R. 18*, p. 475.

[820] ____ The divergence theorem without differentiability conditions. *M.R. 19*, p. 131.

[821] ____ Fourier series in several variables. *M.R. 28*, p. 291.

[822] SHIBATA, K., On boundary values of some pseudo-analytic functions. *M.R. 20*, p. 768.

[823] SICIAK, J., Sur la distribution des points extrémaux dans les ensembles plans. *M.R.21*, p.408.

[824] SIMOLA, I., Potentialtheoretische Randwertprobleme für mehrfach zusammenhängende Gebiete. *M.R. 13*, p. 743.

[825] SINCLAIR, A., The zeros of an analytic function of arbitrarily rapid growth. *M.R. 14*, p. 31.

[826] SINDALOVSKII, G. H., Continuity and differentiability with respect to congruent sets. *M.R. 23A*, p. 324.

[827] ____ On a generalization of derived numbers. *M.R. 23A*, p. 325.

[828] ____ Congruent and asymptotic differentiability. *M.R. 27*, p. 502.

[829] SINGH, S. K., Open Riemann surfaces. *M.R. 27*, p. 61.

[830] SKVORCOV, V. A., Some properties of the *CP*-integral. *M.R. 27*, p. 56.

[831] SLADKOWSKA, J., Sur l'ensemble des points de divergence des séries de Fourier des fonctions continues. *M.R. 22*, p. 27.

[832] ____ Sur l'ensemble des points de divergence des séries de Fourier des fonctions continues. *M.R. 23A*, p. 513.

[833] ŠMIDOV, F. I., Some differential properties of functions of two variables. *M.R. 26*, p. 54.

[834] ____ Some properties of a function of one variable. *M.R. 26*, p. 270.

[835] ŠMUKLER, A. I., Singular integrals and convergence of Fourier series. *M.R. 24A*, p. 179.

[836] ŠNEIDER, A., On series of Walsh functions with monotonic coefficients. *M.R. 10*, p. 34.

[837] ____ On the uniqueness of expansions in Walsh functions. *M.R. 11*, p. 352.

[838] SOKOLIN, A., Concerning a problem of Radó. *M.R. 2*, p. 256.

[839] SOLOMENCEV, E.D., Sur le valeurs limites des fonctions sousharmoniques. *M.R. 21*, p. 1204.

[840] ____ Classes of functions subharmonic on a half-space. *M.R. 25*, p. 618.

[841] ŠREIDER, Y. A., On the Fourier-Stieltjes coefficients of functions of bounded variation. *M.R. 12*, p. 330.

[842] SRIVASTAVA, S. N., On the means of an entire function and its derivatives. *M.R. 26*, p. 280.

[843] STACKELBERG, O. P., On the law of the iterated logarithm. I, II. *M.R. 28*, p. 887.

[844] STEČKIN, S. B., On the theorem of Kolmogorov-Seliverstov. *M.R. 16*, p. 30.

[845] STEČKIN, S. B. and ULJANOV, P. L., On sets of uniqueness. *M.R. 25*, p. 82.

[846] STEIN, E. M., Localization and summability of multiple Fourier series. *M.R. 21*, p. 798.

[847] ____ On limits of sequences of operators. *M.R. 23A*, p. 512.

[848] STEIN, E. M. and WEISS, G., On the theory of harmonic functions of several variables. I. The theory of H^p-spaces. *M.R. 22*, p. 2111.

[849] STEIN, E. M. and ZYGMUND, A., Smoothness and differentiability of functions. *M.R. 24A*, p. 364.

[850] ____ On the differentiability of functions. *M.R. 28*, p. 429.

[851] STEINER, A., Die radialen Randwerte einer Klasse analytischer Funktionen in der oberen Halbebene. *M.R. 17*, p. 1193.

[852] STORVICK, D., On meromorphic functions of bounded characteristic. *M.R. 18*, p. 727.

[853] ____ On pseudo-analytic functions. *M.R. 20*, p. 874.

[854] ____ Cluster sets of pseudo-meromorphic functions. *M.R. 23A*, p. 179.

[855] ____ Relative distances and quasi-conformal mappings. *M.R. 23A*, p. 179.

[856] STREBEL, K., Eine Bemerkung zur Hebbarkeit des Randes einer Riemannschen Fläche. *M.R. 11*, p. 342.

[857] ____ On the maximal dilation of quasiconformal mappings.. *M.R. 17*, p. 473.

[858] STRATILATOVA, M. B., Area in two-dimensional manifolds of bounded curvature as Hausdorff measure. *M.R. 26*, p. 977.

[859] SUITA, N., On some criteria for a set to be of class $N_{\mathfrak{B}}$. *M.R. 26*, p. 278.

[860] SUNOUCHI, G., On the strong summability of Fourier series. *M.R. 7*, p. 247.

[861] ____ Trigonometrical interpolation. *M.R. 12*, p. 821.

[862] ____ A Fourier series which belongs to the class H diverges almost everywhere. *M.R. 15*, p. 27.

[863] ____ On the strong summability of power series and Fourier series. *M.R. 16*, p. 919.

[864] ____ On the Riesz summability of Fourier series. *M.R. 21*, p. 1210.

[865] SUVOROV, G. D., Univalent mappings of plane domains and sets of prime ends of a domain of generalized measure zero. *M.R. 27*, p. 737.

[866] SZ.-NAGY, B., Über die Konvergenz von Reihen orthogonaler Polynome. *M.R. 12*, p. 700.

[867] SZEGÖ, G., On a certain kind of symmetrization and its applications. *M.R. 17*, p. 1074.

[868] SZYBIAK, A., Some properties of plane sets with positive transfinite diameter. *M.R. 18*, p. 730.

[869] TAKAHASHI, S., The law of the iterated logarithm for a gap sequence with infinite gaps. *M.R. 28*, p. 81.

[870] TAIKOV, L. V., Divergence of Fourier series. *M.R. 22*, p. 1666.

[871] ____ Divergence of Fourier series of continuous functions under the rearrangement of a trigonometric system. *M.R. 26*, p. 1268.

[872] TALALJAN, A. A., On convergence of orthogonal series. *M.R. 18*, p. 891.

[873] ____ On the convergence almost everywhere of subsequences of partial sums of general orthogonal series. *M.R. 19*, p. 742.

[874] ____ Summing of series of $L_p[a,b]$ space bases, $p > 1$ by Cesàro's method. *M.R. 21*, p. 48.

[875] ____ The representation of measurable functions by series. *M.R. 23A*, p. 514.

[876] ____ The existence of a trigonometric series universal with respect to its subseries. *M.R. 24A*, p. 179.

[877] ____ Limit functions of series in terms of the bases of an L_p space. *M.R. 27*, p. 347.

[878] ____ Trigonometric series which are universal with respect to subseries. *M.R. 27*, p. 348.

[879] ____ On the convergence and summability almost everywhere of general orthogonal series. *M.R. 27*, p. 544.

[880] ____ Rearranged trigonometrical systems which are systems of convergence in the weak sense. *M.R. 29*, p. 84.

[881] ____ Complete systems of unconditional convergence in the weak sense. *M.R. 29*, p. 503.

[882] TAMURA, J., On a theorem of Tsuji. *M.R. 24A*, p. 39.

[883] TANAKA, C., On the class H_p of functions analytic in the unit circle. *M.R. 19*, p. 130.

[884] ____ Note on the cluster sets of the meromorphic functions. *M.R. 21*, p. 1194.

[885] ____ On functions of class *U*. *M.R. 27*, p. 511.

[886] ____ On Blaschke products in the unit-circle. *M.R. 29*, p. 464.

[887] TANDORI, K., On strong summability of Fourier series. *M.R. 17*, p. 964.

[888] ____ Sur les constantes de Lebesgue des systèmes de fonctions orthogonales et normées. *M.R.19*, p. 412.

[889] ____ Summation of orthogonal series. *M.R. 21*, p. 409.

[890] ____ Über die orthogonalen Funktionen. V. Genaue Weylsche Multiplikatorfolgen. *M.R. 23A*, p. 211.

[891] ____ Über die orthogonalen Funktionen. VI. Eine genaue Bedingung für die starke Summation. *M.R. 23A*, p. 211.

[892] ____ Über die orthogonalen Funktionen. VII. Approximationssätze. *M.R. 23A*, p. 211.

[893] ____ Über die orthogonalen Funktionen. IX. Absolute Summation. *M.R. 24A*, p. 72.

[894] ____ Über ein Problem von G. Alexits. *M.R. 24A*, p. 400.

[895] ____ Über die orthogonalen Funktionen. IV. Starke Summation. *M.R. 24A*, p. 405.

[896] ____ Über die orthogonalen Funktionen. II, III. *M.R. 24A*, p. 648.

[897] ____ Sur la convergence inconditionelle des séries orthogonales. *M.R. 25*, p. 82.

[898] ____ Über Approximationen mit allgemeinen Orthogonalreihen. *M.R. 25*, p. 82.

[899] ____ Über die Divergenz der Orthogonalreihen. *M.R. 25*, p. 463.

[900] ____ Über die orthogonalen Funktionen. X. Unbedingte Konvergenz. *M.R.26*, p. 326.

[901] ____ Über die Konvergenz der Orthogonalreihen. *M.R. 27*, p. 547.

[902] TAYLOR, S. J., The α-dimensional measure of the graph and set of zeros of a Brownian path. *M.R. 17*, p. 595.

[903] ____ On the connexion between Hausdorff measures and generalized capacity. *M.R. 24A*, p. 606.

[904] ____ The exact Hausdorff measure of the sample path for planar Brownian motion. *M.R. 29*, p. 334.

[905] TCHELIDZE, W.G., A necessary and sufficient condition that the double Fourier-Lebesgue series of a function belonging to $L^{(2)}$ should be convergent. *M.R. 1*, p. 226.

[906] TEMKO, K. V., Convex capacity and Fourier series. *M.R. 19*, p. 31.

[907] ____ On absolute convergence of trigonometric series. *M.R. 20*, p. 565.

[908] ____ Equilibrium potential, convex capacity and uniqueness of trigonometric series. *M.R. 22*, p. 1397.

[909] ____ Convex capacity. *M.R. 23A*, p. 58.

[910] ____ Convex capacity and Fourier series. *M.R. 25*, p. 803.

[911] TER-MIKAÈLYAN, T. M., A lower bound for the harmonic measure of a set on certain rectifiable curves. *M.R. 11*, p. 590.

[912] TEVZADZE, N. R., Lebesgue points of a function of two variables. *M.R. 28*, p. 612.

[913] TODA, N. and MATSUMOTO, K., Analytic functions on some Riemann surfaces. *M.R. 28*, p. 45.

[914] TÔKI, Y., On the classification of open Riemann surfaces. *M.R. 14*, p. 864.

[915] ____ On the examples in the classification of open Riemann surfaces. I. *M.R. 15*, p. 519.

[916] TOLSTED, E., Limiting values of subharmonic functions. *M.R. 12*, p. 609.

[917] ____ Non-tangential limits of subharmonic functions. *M.R. 20*, p. 184.

[918] ____ Non-tangential limits of subharmonic functions. II. *M.R.23A*, p. 482.

[919] TOLSTOFF, G., Sur les fonctions bornées vérifiant les conditions de Cauchy-Riemann. *M.R. 4*, p. 136.

[920] ____ The asymptotic derivative of composite functions. *M.R. 12*, p. 487.

[921] ____ On convergence of trigonometric Fourier series for continuous functions. *M.R. 19*, p. 1176.

[922] TOPURIJA, S. B., Summability of Fourier series by the $L^{(p)}$ method and by Voronoi's method. *M.R. 28*, p. 644.

[923] ____ On double lacunary Fourier series. *M.R. 28*, p. 836.

[924] TOVMASJAN, N. E., Some boundary-value problems for the Laplace equation with discontinuous boundary data. *M.R. 28*, p. 633.

[925] TREBUKOVA, N. I., Metric convergence and metric isomorphism. *M.R. 22*, p. 640.

[926] TROHIMČUK, Y., Sur la généralisation de théorème de Picard. *M.R. 21*, p. 23.

[927] TSUCHIKURA, T., A theorem on Riemann sum. Notes on Fourier analysis. XIII. *M.R. 11*, p. 656.

[928] ____ Some remarks on the Riemann sums. *M.R. 13*, p. 543.

[929] ____ Notes on Fourier snalysis. XL. Remark on the Rademacher system. *M.R.13,* p.739.

[930] ____ Absolute Cesàro summability of orthogonal series. *M.R. 15*, p. 417.

[931] ____ Absolute summability of Rademacher series. *M.R. 20*, p. 563.

[932] ____ Some theorems on Fourier series. *M.R. 20*, p. 565.

[933] ____ An application of a method of Marcinkiewicz to the absolute summability of Fourier series. *M.R. 28*, p. 291.

[934] TSUCHIKURA, T. and YANO, S., On the absolute convergence of trigonometrical series. *M.R. 12*, p. 174.

[935] TSUJI, M., Nevanlinna's fundamental theorems and Ahlfors' theorem on the number of asymptotic values. *M.R. 7*, p. 288.

[936] ____ On the Green's function. *M.R. 8*, p. 203.

[937] ____ On the behaviour of a meromorphic function in the neighbourhood of a closed set of capacity zero. *M.R. 8*, p. 373.

[938] ____ Theory of meromorphic functions in a neighbourhood of a closed set of capacity zero. *M.R. 8*, p. 508.

[939] ____ On the cluster set of a meromorphic function. *M.R. 8*, p. 508.

[940] ____ Some metrical theorems on Fuchsian groups. *M.R. 10*, p. 365.

[941] ____ On the boundary value of a bounded analytic function of several complex variables. *M.R. 11*, p. 345.

[942] ____ On the Green's function associated with a Fuchsian group. *M.R. 11*, p. 511.

[943] ____ Beurling's theorem on exceptional sets. *M.R. 12*, p. 692.

[944] ____ Some metrical theorems on Fuchsian groups. *M.R. 13*, p. 125.

[945] ____ Some theorems on open Riemann surfaces. *M.R. 13*, p. 338.

[946] ____ On meromorphic functions with essential singularities of logarithmic capacity zero. *M.R. 13*, p. 453.

[947] ____ On the uniformization of an algebraic function of genus $p \geq 2$. *M.R. 14*, p. 157.

[948] ____ Wiman's theorem on integral functions of order $< \frac{1}{2}$. *M.R. 14*, p. 259.

[949] ____ Fundamental theorems in potential theory. *M.R. 14*, p. 644.

[950] ____ On the capacity of general Cantor sets. *M.R. 15*, p. 309.

[951] ____ On the exceptional set of a certain harmonic function in a unit sphere. *M.R.15*, p.703.

[952] ____ Theory of meromorphic functions on an open Riemann surface with null boundary. *M.R. 15*, p. 518.

[953] ____ A metrical theorem on the singular set of a linear group of Schottky type. *M.R. 16*, p. 349.

[954] ____ On the radial order of a certain regular function in a unit circle. *M.R. 16*, p. 809.

[955] ____ Function of *U*-class and its applications. *M.R. 17*, p. 600.

[956] ____ A metrical theorem on conformal mapping. *M.R. 17*, p. 725.

[957] ____ Littlewood's theorem on subharmonic functions in a unit circle. *M.R. 18*, p. 122.

[958] ____ A simple proof of a theorem of Erdös and Gillis on the transfinite diameter. *M.R. 18*, p. 650.

[959] ____ On a Riemann surface, which is conformally equivalent to a Riemann surface with a finite spherical area. *M.R. 19*, p. 1043.

[960] ____ On the capacity of a set in the space of regular functions and its applications. *M.R. 21*, p. 516.

[961] ____ Potential theory in modern function theory. *M.R. 22*, p. 958.

[962] ____ A theorem on the boundary behaviour of a meromorphic function in $|z| < 1$. *M.R. 22*, p. 1899.

[963] TUMARKIN, G. C., On convergent sequences of analytic functions. *M.R. 11*, p. 338.

[964] ____ Conditions for convergence of boundary values of a sequence of analytic functions which use convergence of the moduli. *M.R. 16*, p. 686.

[965] TUMARKIN, G. C. and HAVINSON, S. J., On the removing of singularities for analytic functions of a certain class (class *D*). *M.R. 20*, p. 17.

[966] TUMURA, Y., Recherches sur la distribution des valeurs des fonctions analytiques. *M.R. 8*, p. 24.

[967] TZODIKS, V. M., On sets of points where the derivative is finite or infinite correspondingly. *M.R. 19*, p. 734.

[968] UGAHERI, T., On the general potential and capacity. *M.R. 13*, p. 743.

[969] ULJANOV, P. L., Generalization of a theorem of Marcinkiewicz. *M.R.16*, p.30.

[970] ____ On unconditional convergence almost everywhere. *M.R. 18*, p. 803.

[971] ____ Permutations of a trigonometric system. *M.R. 20*, p. 310.

[972] ____ Undonditional convergence and summability. *M.R. 13*, p. 413.

[973] ____ Strongly undonditionally convergent series. *M.R. 22*, p. 1181.

[974] ____ Divergent Fourier series of class $L^p (p \geq 2)$. *M.R. 22*, p. 1667.

[975] ____ Convergence and summability. *M.R. 24A*, p. 283.

[976] ____ On series in a permuted trigonometric system. *M.R. 24A*, p. 287.

[977] ____ Divergent series over a Haar system and over bases. *M.R. 24A*, p. 521.

[978] ____ Exact Weyl factors for unconditional convergence. *M.R. 24A*, p. 522.

[979] ____ Weyl factors for unconditional convergence. *M.R. 26*, p. 540.

[980] ____ Solved and unsolved problems in the theory of trigonometric and orthogonal series. *M.R. 28*, p. 834.

[981] ULLEMAR, L., Über die Existenz der automorphen Funktionen mit beschränktem Dirichletintegral. *M.R. 14*, p. 470.

[982] ULLMAN, J. L., On Tchebycheff polynomials. *M.R. 21*, p. 1365.

[983] ULLRICH, E., Betragflächen mit ausgezeichneten Krümmungsverhalten. *M.R. 13*, p. 124.

[984] VASILESCO, F., Sur une notion nouvelle de capacité d'un ensemble. *M.R. 6*, p. 87.

[985] ____ Sur la notion de capacité d'un ensemble borné quelconque. *M.R. 7*, p. 121.

[986] VERBLUNSKY, S., On a fundamental formula of potential theory. *M.R. 12*, p. 703.

[987] ____ An outline of the theory of F_2 series. *M.R. 19*, p. 412.

[988] VIOLA, T., Sur la possibilité de compléter la definition d'une fonction donnée sur un domaine ouvert, par tendance à la limite vers la frontière du domaine. *M.R. 13*, p. 925.

[989] VIRTANEN, K. J., Über die Existenz von beschränkten harmonischen Funktionen auf offenen Riemannschen Flächen. *M.R. 12*, p. 403.

[990] VITUŠKIN, A. G., Analytic capacity of sets and some of its properties. *M.R. 21*, p. 391.

[991] ____ Some theorems on the possibility of a uniform approximation of continuous functions by analytic functions. *M.R. 21*, p. 391.

[992] ____ Example of a set of positive length but of zero analytic capacity. *M.R. 22*, p. 1628.

[993] VOICHICK, M., Ideals and invariant subspaces of analytic functions. *M.R. 28*, p. 803.

[994] VOLKOVYSKII, L., Contemporary investigations in the theory of Riemann surfaces. *M.R. 19*, p. 539.

[995] VOSTRECOV, B. A., On the existence of boundary values and on the integral representation of functions analytic in the unit circle. *M.R. 10*, p. 523.

[996] VÄISÄLÄ, J., On the null-sets for extremal distances. *M.R. 26*, p. 979.

[997] WALFISH, A., Über einige Orthogonalreihen. *M.R. 3*, p. 108.

[998] WALLIN, H., On Bohr's spectrum of a function. *M.R. 23A*, p. 517.

[999] ____ Studies in potential theory. *M.R. 27*, p. 514.

[1000] ____ Continuous functions and potential theory. *M.R. 29*, p. 469.

[1001] WALSH, J. L., Overconvergence, degree of convergence, and zeros of sequences of analytic functions. *M.R. 8*, p. 201.

[1002] ____ On the location of the critical points of harmonic measure. *M.R. 8*, p. 461.

[1003] ____ Note on the location of the critical points of harmonic functions. *M.R. 9*, p. 432.

[1004] WALSH, J. L. and EVANS, J. P., Note on the distribution of zeros of extremal polynomials. *M.R. 15*, p. 954.

[1005] WANG, F. T., A note on the summability of lacunary partial sums of Fourier series. *M.R. 2*, p. 361.

[1006] ____ Note on the absolute summability of trigonometrical series. *M.R. 4*, p. 217.

[1007] ____ The absolute Cesàro summability of trigonometrical series. *M.R. 4*, p. 37.

[1008] ____ On Riesz summability of Fourier series. III. *M.R. 11*, p. 27.

[1009] WANG, S.-L., On the functions represented by Rademacher series. *M.R. 29*, p. 85.

[1010] WATANABE, S., On stable processes with boundary conditions. *M.R. 26*, p. 373.

[1011] WEISS, G., Harmonic analysis in several variables. Theory of H^p-spaces. *M.R. 25*, p. 646.

[1012] WEISS, M., On the law of the iterated logarithm for uniformly bounded orthonormal systems. *M.R. 21*, p. 1087.

[1013] ____ The law of the iterated logarithm for lacunary trigonometric series. *M.R. 21*, p. 1370.

[1014] WEISS, M. and WEISS, G., A derivation of the main results of the theory of H^p-spaces. *M.R. 28*, p. 262.

[1015] WEISS, M. and ZYGMUND, A., On the existence of conjugate functions of higher order. *M.R. 22*, p. 665.

[1016] WEISS, M., On symmetric derivatives in L^p. *M.R. 28*, p. 1024.

[1017] WILSON, R., The directions of strongest growth of an integral function of finite order and mean type. *M.R. 19*, p. 949.

[1018] WINTNER, A., On Fourier averages. *M.R. 3*, p. 109.

[1019] WITTICH, H., Neuere Untersuchungen über eindeutige analytische Funktionen. *M.R. 17*, p. 1067.

[1020] ____ Defekte Werte eindeutiger analytischer Funktionen. *M.R. 21*, p. 390.

[1021] WOLF, F., Ein Eindeutigkeitssatz für analytische Funktionen. *M.R. 2*, p. 81.

[1022] ____ On summable trigonometrical series: an extension of uniqueness theorems. *M.R. 1*, p. 225.

[1023] WOLFF, J., Deux théorèmes sur la dérivée d'une fonction holomorphe univalente et bornée dans un demi-plan au voisinage de la frontière. *M.R. 5*, p. 259.

[1024] ____ Inégalités remplies par les dérivées des fonctions holomorphes univalentes et bornées dans un demi-plan. *M.R. 5*, p. 234.

[1025] ____ Inégalités remplies par les fonctions univalentes. *M.R. 7*, p. 379.

[1026] WOLFOWITZ, J., Convergence of the empiric distribution function on half-spaces. *M.R. 22*, p. 1953.

[1027] WOLONTIS, V., Properties of conformal invariants. *M.R. 14*, p. 36.

[1028] WOOLF, W. B., The boundary behaviour of meromorphic functions. *M.R. 26*, p. 748.

[1029] YANO, K., A note on absolute Cesàro summability of Fourier series. *M.R. 22*, p. 2113.

[1030] YANO, S., Notes on Fourier analysis. XV. On the absolute convergence of trigonometrical series. *M.R. 11*, p. 348.

[1031] ____ Notes on Fourier analysis (XIX): A remark on Riemann sums. *M.R. 12*, p. 811.

[1032] ____ On Walsh-Fourier series. *M.R. 13*, p. 550.

[1033] ____ Note on Fourier analysis. XXXI. Cesàro summability of Fourier series. *M.R. 14*, p. 267.

[1034] ____ Cesàro summability of Fourier series. *M.R. 14*, p. 552.

[1035] ____ Cesàro summability of Fourier series. *M.R. 15*, p. 788.

[1036] YOSIDA, K., On the representation of functions by Fourier integrals. *M.R. 7*, p. 248.

[1037] YOSIDA, T., On the behaviour of a pseudo-regular function in a neighbourhood of a closed set of capacity zero. *M.R. 14*, p. 365.

[1038] YOUNG, G. S., Types of ambiguous behaviour of analytic functions. *M.R. 24A*, p. 374.

[1039] YUJOBO, Z., A theorem on Fuchsian groups. *M.R. 11*, p. 96.

[1040] ____ A theorem on Fourier series. *M.R. 16*, p. 241.

[1041] ____ On absolutely continuous functions of two or more variables in the Tonelli sense and quasi-conformal mappings in the A. Mori sense. *M.R. 17*, p. 836.

[1042] ZAANEN, A. C., Some examples in weak sequential convergence. *M.R. 24A*, p. 398.

[1043] ZAHARJAN, V. S., On a uniqueness theorem. *M.R. 28*, p. 436.

[1044] ____ Uniqueness theorems for certain classes of functions holomorphic in the circle. *M.R. 28*, p. 436.

[1045] ____ The radial limit values of a class of functions meromorphic in the circle. *M.R. 28*, p. 1002.

[1046] ZAHORSKI, Z., Punktmengen, in welchen eine stetige Funktion nicht differentierbar ist. *M.R. 3*, p. 73.

[1047] ____ Un problème de la théorie des ensembles et des fonctions. *M.R. 8*, p. 148.

[1048] ____ Sur les ensembles des points de divergence de certaines intégrales singulières. *M.R. 9*, p. 89.

[1049] ____ On a problem of M. F. Leja. *M.R. 10*, p. 117.